basic
industrial
electricity

by VAN VALKENBURGH,
NOOGER & NEVILLE, INC.

VOL. 2

JOHN F. RIDER PUBLISHER, INC., NEW YORK
a division of HAYDEN PUBLISHING COMPANY, INC.

PREFACE

COMMON-CORE

Great as the emphasis on electronics is today, a very large proportion of industrial effort is still thoroughly grounded in the more elementary electrical techniques. Recognition of this fact has been given proper weight in the planning and preparation of this "COMMON-CORE" Series on Basic Industrial Electricity.

There is no doubt that any person, having behind him the knowledge, understanding, and skill afforded by our COMMON-CORE course of instruction in Basic Electricity, can put such training to important and immediate use in industry today. Without more, the learner is ready to make a start. A transitional step at this point is often most helpful, however.

With this thought, our two books presented as an addition to the COMMON-CORE Series and entitled "Basic Industrial Electricity," have been developed as a logical applications course following Volumes 1 through 5 of our Basic Electricity. Also, in this way there is here provided the necessary foundation for future work in automatic control.

All industrial processes and systems are said to have two essential ingredients: (1) Work handling of the physical material within the process and (2) Information necessarily associated with the handling operations. These Basic Industrial Electricity books concern themselves with the electrical devices for work handling and information gathering which, in turn, lay the groundwork for further understanding and mastery of integrated industrial control processes and the industrial control computer.

Starting out with the fundamental areas of Power Distribution and Illumination, a host of industrial usages -- Electromechanical Machinery Control, Electromechanical Servo Control Systems, Fluid Control Devices, Industrial Fluid Control Systems, Process Control and Product Inspection, Remote Monitoring and Control, Electric Welding and Heating, and various other Miscellaneous Industrial Control Systems -- all are analyzed and explained, building only within the background encompassed by our COMMON-CORE course of instruction entitled "Basic Electricity." Naturally, there are many equivalent and far more sophisticated electronics applications and these, too, are being treated by us in a similar manner for later publication, using as a background our COMMON-CORE courses in both Basic Electricity and Basic Electronics.

Here, then, in an easy-to-understand, interesting-to-read, semi-programed treatment are two volumes showing present-day industrial applications of Basic Electricity. Also available separately to supplement these texts are a series of criterion multiple-choice questions with a correlated TRAINER-TESTER auto-instructional programing device.

VAN VALKENBURGH, NOOGER & NEVILLE, INC.

New York, N.Y.
October, 1962

CONTENTS

ELECTRICITY IN INDUSTRY

Introduction

In Volume 1 you learned about some of the various fluid control devices that are available. Now you are ready to find out how these devices are used in industrial fluid control systems. This section contains analyses of typical industrial heating, refrigeration, air conditioning, and liquid and gas processing systems. The first three of these are vital to the operation of nearly all modern industries, and liquid and gas processing systems are widely used in food, chemical, pharmaceutical and oil refining industries.

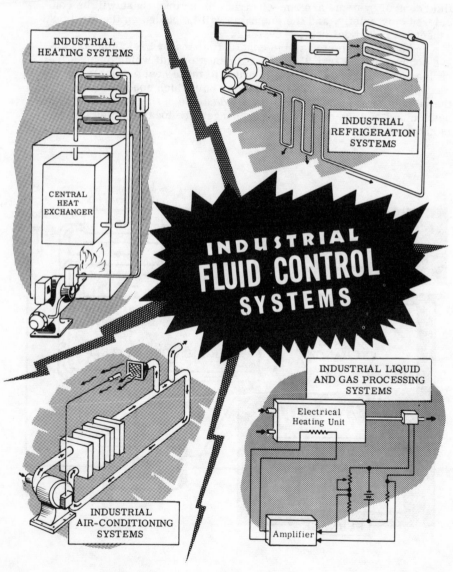

Industrial Heating Systems

Industrial heating systems are examples of arrangements in which a fluid is used as the medium for transferring heat from one place to another. In a heating system, a fluid, such as water, steam or air, is heated by a furnace and transmitted through pipes or ducts to the areas where heat is desired. (Electric heating will be treated in Section 10.) Since the heat-transmitting medium is a fluid, many of the fluid control devices that were discussed in Section 6 will now be seen in practical use. As was mentioned in that section, many of the components used in fluid control systems are non-electrical in nature; these will be considered only briefly, and the emphasis will be placed on the electrical aspects of industrial heating systems.

Industrial heating systems contain four major basic components and subsystems. First, there is a combustion unit which burns a fuel, such as coal, coke, oil or gas, in order to make heat available for use. Next, there is a central heat-exchanger unit which conducts a fluid into the vicinity of the heat, so that the fluid can be heated. Both the combustion unit and the central heat exchanger are located in the unit that is known as the "furnace."

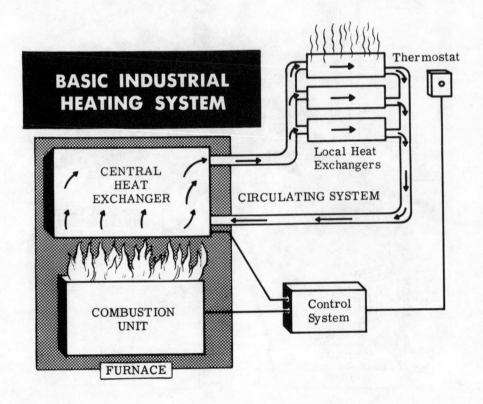

Industrial Heating Systems (continued)

Then there is a circulation system which moves the heated fluid from the vicinity of the combustion unit to the locations where the heat is required. At these locations, the local heat exchangers, such as radiators, transfer the heat from the fluid to the area to be heated. The cooled fluid then flows back through the circulation system to the central heat exchanger near the combustion unit, so that it can be reheated and recirculated. Finally, there is a system of controls that provides for safe, efficient, and coordinated operation of the entire system. The electrical aspects of each of these four major components and subsystems will be reviewed in this section.

In the usual coal or coke combustion unit, an electric motor drives a gear system which, in turn, rotates a screw-type mechanism similar in basic construction to that found in a meat grinder. The rotation of the screw mechanism pulls coal out of a hopper and forces it into the furnace fire box at a rate that is suitable for supplying the required amount of heat. The electric motor also drives an air blower which sends blasts of air into the fire box to assure efficient burning.

The coal-feeding mechanism and air blower do not operate continuously. The electric motor is started when the temperature in either the central heat exchanger or the area being heated drops below the desired level. This is accomplished by means of thermostats. The same controller turns off the electric motor when the central heat exchanger or the heated area reaches the desired temperature. Such control is not adequate, however, for satisfactory operation, since the fire in the furnace may go out if there is a long interval between the times that the coal-feeding mechanism is turned on by a thermostat. To make sure that enough coal is supplied to keep the fire burning, a timing unit, such as is described in Section 4, periodically turns on the coal feed and accompanying air blast for a short time. The duration of the on and off periods is determined by the details of the installation, and the periods are set to assure continued burning without unnecessary fuel consumption.

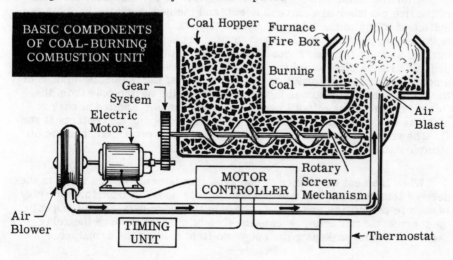

BASIC COMPONENTS OF COAL-BURNING COMBUSTION UNIT

Coal Hopper

Furnace Fire Box

Burning Coal

Air Blast

Gear System

Electric Motor

Rotary Screw Mechanism

MOTOR CONTROLLER

Air Blower

TIMING UNIT

Thermostat

Industrial Heating Systems (continued)

A somewhat different type of arrangement is used in oil-fired furnaces. In such a system, a pump is used to take oil from a storage tank and bring it to the combustion unit. In order to burn efficiently, the oil must be broken down into an extremely fine spray that is mixed with large volumes of air. This is accomplished by a nozzle that operates on the same general principle as a paint sprayer; that is, by blowing a stream of air past the open end of a tube out of which oil is flowing. A fairly complex arrangement is required to provide safe flame control.

When the oil spray is turned on by the thermostat, it is ignited by an electric arc across two electrodes that are in the path of the spray. The complete arrangement is shown in the diagram; the major control elements include a thermostat in the area to be heated, a temperature-sensitive switch (called a "flame detector") in the furnace smoke stack, and a relay. When the combustion unit is off, the bi-metal element of the flame detector is cold, and the attached switch pole touches the "cold" contact. When the area that is to be heated becomes cooler than the setting on its local thermostat, this thermostat closes and the relay coil is energized, resulting in the closing of the pairs of contacts A and B. These contacts supply voltage to the motor that drives the oil pump and the air blower. These contacts also supply voltage to the ignition transformer through thermostat contacts C in the flame detector. A high voltage of several thousand volts, or more, is generated across the secondary winding of the ignition transformer, causing an electric arc to jump across the electrodes. This arc ignites the oil spray, and the flame is directed into a chamber made of fire brick or similar heat-resistant material. The heat that is generated raises the temperature of the water or air that is used to transfer heat to the area that is to be warmed.

After the flame has been on for about one or two minutes, the walls of the fire chamber are extremely hot, and the heat radiated by them is sufficient to ignite the oil spray before it strikes the walls. Thus, there is no further need for the arc, and turning it off prevents unnecessary burning away of the electrodes. This is accomplished by the temperature-sensitive flame detector in the smoke stack. As the temperature in the smoke stack rises for about one or two minutes, the bi-metal element in the flame detector becomes heated and moves the switch pole from the "cold" contact to the "hot" contact. Voltage is now applied across resistance heater 1, and the heat that is generated opens the contacts C and D. The voltage to the ignition transformer is now turned off, and the oil spray continues to burn.

When the heat exchanger or the area that is being heated rises to the desired temperature, the thermostat contacts open. A transformer relay is used to permit the use of low voltage in the thermostat circuit. Opening the thermostat contacts prevents the flow of current through the relay secondary, thus weakening the magnetic field holding the armature.

Industrial Heating Systems (continued)

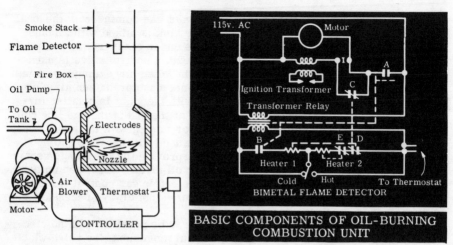

BASIC COMPONENTS OF OIL-BURNING COMBUSTION UNIT

Contacts A and B immediately open, and the flow of oil and air is stopped. The flame in the fire chamber goes out. Now the bi-metal flame detector element in the stack cools rapidly and moves the switch pole back to the "cold" contact. Heater element 1 cools and closes switch contacts C and D. The combustion unit will start once again when the thermostat contacts close again.

Up to this time, only the normal operation of the system has been considered. No mention has been made of the purpose of heater element 2 and the associated contacts E. These units are safety devices which are used to turn off the flow of oil and air in the event that a defect in the ignition transformer or the electrodes prevents the arc from starting, and the oil spray is not ignited within one or two minutes after the spray is started. If the arc should happen to go on after a longer period, there might be enough free oil and oil vapor in the fire chamber to cause a serious explosion.

The operation of the safety circuit will now be described. Remember that as long as the bi-metal element of the stack flame detector remains cold, the switch pole touches the "cold" contact. This permits current to flow through the closed pairs of contacts marked D and E and then on through resistance heater element 2. If the bi-metal element is heated by hot gases in the stack, normal operation takes place as described previously. If the bi-metal element is not heated, current continues to flow through resistance heater element 2. After about one or two minutes of such heating, switch contacts E open and are held open by a latching device. The opening of these contacts de-energizes the transformer relay coil, and contacts A and B open, stopping the motor which pumps oil and air. Because of the latching device on contacts E, the thermostat cannot start operation again until the latching device has been manually released. This closes contacts E and permits the starting cycle to begin again. Now if the flame fails to start after one or two tries, the operator can inspect the mechanism and repair the defect.

Industrial Heating Systems (continued)

In a gas-fired combustion unit, a stream of gas coming from the local gas company's supply line or from a storage tank is mixed with air and ignited to form a hot flame. Since the gas is under pressure, no pump is required to force it towards the flame. Instead, a control valve is used to turn the flow of gas on and off as required. When large amounts of gas are to be burned rapidly, as in a large furnace, a motor-driven air blower can be used to supply the air that is mixed with the gas. In smaller furnaces the rush of gas through a constriction at the end of the gas line can be used to draw outside air into the nozzle for mixing with the gas.

A wide variety of control systems can be used with gas-fired combustion units. At one extreme the control can be provided by an arrangement that is almost identical to that described for oil-fired combustion units. The only significant differences are that an electric gas control valve is used instead of an oil pump, and an air blower is not always necessary, as mentioned in the preceding paragraph.

At the other extreme, adequate control can be provided with no electric control devices of any kind. In such an arrangement, the valve which regulates the flow of gas can be controlled by the pressure changes in a gas-filled temperature-measuring bulb which replaces the thermostat. An electric arc is not required to ignite the stream of mixed gas and air coming out of the nozzle; a pilot light that is on continuously can be used instead. An electric stack switch is not the only method of providing safety if the gas and air mixture coming out of the nozzle fails to ignite. One possible arrangement is to have the gas flow control valve equipped with a spring motor or dashpot. When this valve is opened by the gas-filled temperature-measuring thermostat bulb, it will automatically close in approximately 10 to 30 seconds unless the stack flame detector device operates to hold it in an open position. This flame detector can be a bi-metal element or a gas-filled bulb; when heated by the hot stack gases, its expansion applies the pressure necessary to hold the gas flow control valve in an open position.

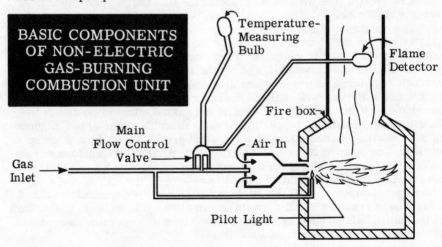

BASIC COMPONENTS OF NON-ELECTRIC GAS-BURNING COMBUSTION UNIT

Temperature-Measuring Bulb

Flame Detector

Fire box

Main Flow Control Valve

Air In

Gas Inlet

Pilot Light

Industrial Heating Systems (continued)

The heat-exchanger portions of a furnace are designed mainly to use hot water, steam or hot air as a heat exchange medium. In hot-water and steam furnaces, a water-filled container surrounds the combustion chamber and absorbs heat from it. Some heat exchangers, popularly known as "boilers," add to the heat-absorption of the water jacket by also having water-filled tubes around the walls of the combustion chamber to add to the heat-absorbing area. The construction of steam and hot-water heat exchangers is similar, the major difference being that steam units are constructed with much stronger walls, to resist the pressure of the steam that forms above the water surface.

The control systems for hot-water and steam heat exchangers are quite similar. A typical hot-water system arrangement is shown in the diagram. Water is required to replace losses that take place in the fluid-circulating portion of the system. This water enters the heat exchanger through a check valve, a pressure reducing valve and a pressure relief valve. The check valve prevents the water expansion, caused by heating, from forcing hot water out through the supply line. The pressure reducing valve prevents excessively high water pressures in the supply line from causing the heat exchanger to operate at pressures higher than desired. Finally, the pressure relief valve provides protection against excessively high pressures in the heat exchanger in the event that there is a failure in the combustion unit shut-off device.

Since water expands when it is heated, undesirably high pressures would develop in the system unless some method were provided for allowing the water to expand against some readily compressed material. An expansion tank, filled mainly with air, connected to the top of the exchanger serves this purpose. When the water in the exchanger expands, the water level in the expansion tank rises, and the air is compressed easily without causing an undesirably high rise in pressure.

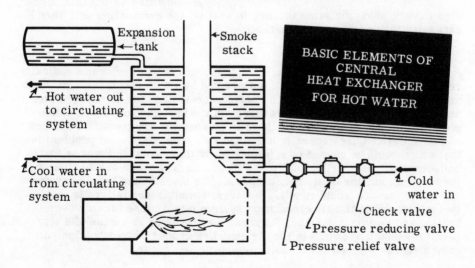

Expansion tank — Smoke stack

BASIC ELEMENTS OF CENTRAL HEAT EXCHANGER FOR HOT WATER

Hot water out to circulating system

Cool water in from circulating system

Cold water in
Check valve
Pressure reducing valve
Pressure relief valve

Industrial Heating Systems (continued)

Hot-water central heat exchangers generally provide at least one additional protective device. The type most generally used is a temperature-sensitive switch element (called an "aquastat") that is immersed in the water of the heat exchanger. Regardless of the temperature in the area that is being heated, the switch elements open and turn off the combustion unit when the water temperature rises to 180 to 200 degrees Fahrenheit. This prevents the water from reaching the boiling point, where steam would be formed and dangerously high pressures would be generated. If a non-electrical control is desired, as in some gas-fired furnaces, protection is provided by means of an expansion bulb arrangement which drives a valve that shuts off the flow of gas to the combustion unit.

In a steam heat exchanger, the arrangement is quite similar to that of the hot-water type. A noteworthy difference is that the water level does not extend to the top of the heat exchanger, and space for the formation of steam is thus provided. The pressure relief valve is normally placed above the water level so that it can release steam, instead of water, to rapidly lower excessive pressures to the safe operating region. As in the case of the hot-water system, a temperature switch that monitors water or steam temperature can be used to shut off the combustion unit when excessive temperatures are reached. However, the most usual type of protective arrangement is a pressure-sensitive switch that operates in very much the same manner to shut off the combustion unit when excessive temperatures are reached.

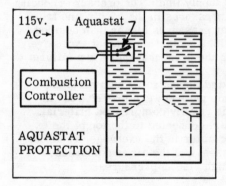

In a hot-air heat exchanger, the number of control devices is radically reduced. The combustion unit is surrounded by a metal shell through which air is circulated for heating. The various provisions for supplying water and for preventing excessive pressures in the heat exchanger are completely eliminated. In general, there is no need for any protective devices, and such devices are generally not employed. One significant problem is that which could be caused by a failure in the thermostat in the area that is being heated. Ordinarily, such a failure would only cause overheating in the building, and the faulty condition would be investigated before any danger in the furnace would result. However, simultaneous failure in that thermostat and in the air circulation system might cause furnace overheating and resultant damage. This can be prevented by means of a temperature-sensitive switch in the air chamber around the combustion unit; combustion is stopped if excessive temperatures occur.

Industrial Heating Systems (continued)

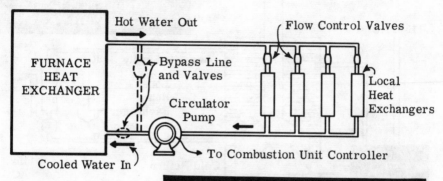

CIRCULATING SYSTEM

The diagram shows a complete control arrangement for a typical hot-water heating system. The operation of the combustion unit and furnace heat exchanger have been described previously, and the present discussion will be restricted to overall system operation.

In operation, hot water from the furnace heat exchanger is pumped through the radiators or other types of local heat exchangers in the building. The water loses some of its heat to the air in the building and flows back to the furnace heat exchanger. It is sometimes undesirable to have the radiators or other types of local heat exchangers in the building operate at the furnace water temperature of 180 to 200 degrees Fahrenheit. Cooler circulating water can be obtained by bypassing most of the return water around the furnace and mixing it with the very hot water from the heat exchanger. The bypass line and the valves for controlling the amount of mixing are shown in dotted lines.

In a large building there are many different areas to be heated. Each of these areas may have a different amount of heat loss to the outside, and each area may have its own most desirable comfort conditions. To provide for such differences, each area has its own thermostat and its own circulator pump. When the temperature in an area falls below the desired level, the thermostat starts the circulator pump. This circulates hot water through the local heat exchangers and raises the area temperature. When the temperature reaches the desired level, the circulator pump goes off. No more hot water is pumped through the local heat exchangers, and the temperature stops rising. Thus, temperature in each area is controlled by its own thermostat.

ALTERNATE CIRCULATING CONTROL

Hot Supply

Local Heat Exchanger

Local Circulator Pump

Cold Return

115v. AC

Industrial Heating Systems (continued)

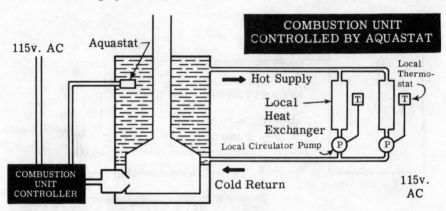

An alternate, but equivalent, arrangement is to have one large circulator pump at the heat exchanger and individual control valves in each building area. The local thermostats open and close their local control valves, and each area is heated according to its own requirements.

With all of these thermostats operating independently of each other, it would not be practical to have any of them control the starting and stopping of the combustion unit. It is much more logical to have each local thermostat and its associated circulator draw hot water as required from the furnace heat exchanger, and use some other means of combustion control. The most practical method is the use of a temperature-sensitive switch (aquastat) immersed in the boiler water. When large amounts of hot water are pumped out of the boiler by the various circulators and corresponding amounts of cooled water are returned to the boiler, the boiler water temperature begins to drop. When the boiler temperature falls below the level required for efficient heating, say 160 degrees, the immersed switch element turns on the combustion unit. Heat is supplied until the boiler water reaches the temperature of 180 to 200 degrees, and then the temperature-sensitive switch turns the combustion unit off. Since this immersed switch provides protection against overheating as one of its two functions, it can be used to replace the heat-exchanger overheat-preventing aquastat mentioned earlier in the review of furnace heat exchanger safety devices.

There is one additional system control that is sometimes used. If all circulators in the plant heating system should happen to be on at the same time, a very long period of time might be required before the combustion unit could raise the boiler water temperature to the desired upper level. On very cold days the boiler water temperature could remain at a temperature well below 160 degrees for extended periods of time. Such low-temperature operation chills the walls of the combustion chamber and the entrance to the smoke stack, causing the condensation of smoke residues on these surfaces and making more frequent furnace cleaning necessary.

This can be prevented by having the aquastat in the boiler water drive two separate switch contacts in the combustion controller.

Industrial Heating Systems (continued)

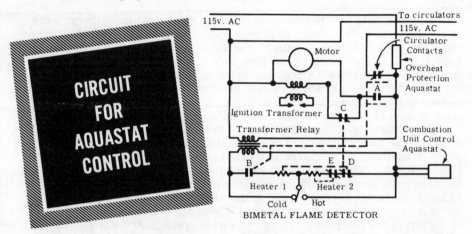

BIMETAL FLAME DETECTOR

One pair of contacts turns the combustion unit on and off as described earlier. The other pair supplies line voltage to the local circulators when the combustion unit is off and cuts off line voltage from the circulators when the combustion unit is on. The thermostat connected to each circulator continues to operate as described earlier, but the combustion unit central heat exchanger aquastat is able to turn off all circulators even if their thermostats have turned them on. Thus, the aquastat prevents the boiler water temperature from dropping below the desired level in spite of the operation of the local thermostats.

There are many methods for distributing steam through a building. The basic factor that is common to all of these systems is that the pressure of the steam drives it to the various radiators or other local heat exchangers throughout the building. When the steam loses its heat, it condenses back into the form of water, which is returned by gravity flow or by pump to the furnace heat exchanger for reheating.

When only one thermostat is used to control the temperature in a building, the control arrangement is simple; that thermostat starts and stops the combustion unit. If the building is large and separate thermostat temperature controls are required in different areas, the control arrangement is quite similar to that for the hot-water heating system described above. Thermostats can control the flow of steam to different parts of the building by opening and closing electrically driven control valves.

In a hot-air heating system, the general control arrangement is also very similar to those described for hot-water and steam systems. In a one-thermostat system, the thermostat turns on both the combustion unit and a main circulator fan. In a large building, a number of thermostats can be used. Each thermostat controls either a circulator fan or an electrically driven damper. The damper is a large butterfly valve which opens and closes the hot air duct. When dampers are used, a main air blower is used near the furnace. In systems where many thermostats are used, the combustion unit is turned on and off by a temperature-sensitive switch in the air chamber surrounding the furnace.

Industrial Refrigeration Systems

You are quite familiar with the fact that refrigeration is the process of making food cold in order to preserve it. You know that refrigerator units are used in homes, in stores where food is sold, and in food-processing plants. Refrigeration is also used in the drug industry in the manufacture of antibiotics such as penicillin, and in aluminum parts factories in the chilling process used to produce hardening. It is also used in food and blood plasma dehydration, in the manufacture of rubber and a wide variety of chemical products and to liquify gases such as oxygen.

As in the case of industrial heating systems, industrial refrigeration systems are also examples of apparatus for transferring heat from one place to another. In refrigeration, heat is removed by a fluid known as a "refrigerant." The cold fluid is circulated around the material that is to be made cold, and a heat exchange takes place in which some of the heat from the material is transferred to the fluid. The slightly warmed fluid flows back to the heat extractor, and the process continues.

Most of the components in refrigeration systems are non-electrical, and the electrical control systems that are used are quite elementary in nature. Refrigeration systems are reviewed here mainly because they are widely used and are very important in industrial processes.

Although there are many methods for production of cold by heat removal, only the vapor-compression and absorption techniques are practical at present. Both of these methods depend upon the physical fact that liquids absorb heat when they evaporate and expand to the form of a vapor, and vapor loses heat when it is condensed back into the form of a liquid. Although most liquids, including water, can be used for this process, the most commonly used refrigerants are gases which can be liquefied by the application of moderate pressure and slight cooling. Ammonia gas is widely used in industrial refrigeration applications. It is low in cost and highly efficient, but it is unsuitable for use in applications such as air conditioning and domestic refrigeration, since it is foul smelling and toxic should any escape. For such applications Freon gas is most suitable at present.

Both the vapor-compression system and the vapor-absorption system make use of an "evaporator" unit in which the liquefied gas expands and absorbs heat, and a "condenser" unit in which the gas is changed back to liquid form and loses heat. The basic difference between the two systems is the method used to transfer the fluid from the evaporator to the condenser. In the absorption system, the transfer is accomplished by means of a chemical or physical process; no pumps are used and no electrical controls are required. In the vapor-compression system, the transfer is accomplished by means of a pump, and electrical controls are used to turn on the pump and auxiliary devices.

The illustration shows a schematic flow diagram of a basic vapor-compression refrigeration system. You can see that a pump is used to transfer the vaporized fluid from the evaporator to the condenser. A piston pump such as was described previously can be used for this purpose when the refrigerant is ammonia, sulphur dioxide, carbon dioxide or high-pressure Freon (known as Freon 12).

Industrial Refrigeration Systems (continued)

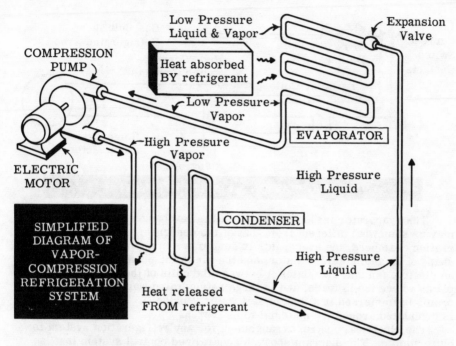

When moderate-pressure Freon 21 is used, a rotating-vane type of pump is suitable. With a low-pressure refrigerant, such as Freon 11, a centrifugal type of pump can be used.

The pump removes vapor from the evaporator and forces it into the condenser. Since there is an expansion valve with only an extremely small opening to permit the refrigerant to escape into the evaporator, the vapor is forced into the condenser faster than it can escape through the valve opening. As a result, there is a high-pressure region inside the condenser, and a low-pressure region inside the evaporator.

The condenser is actually a high-pressure heat exchanger. It is a long tube formed into a shape very much like an automobile radiator, so that it can easily dissipate the heat from the refrigerant. In domestic refrigerators, normal air circulation provides adequate cooling of the condenser coils. In industrial systems, an air blast or water stream accomplishes this cooling more efficiently. In any event, when the compressed refrigerant vapor is cooled, it returns to the form of a liquid and releases even more heat. This liquid accumulates in the lower portion of the condenser. In systems containing large amounts of liquefied refrigerant, the liquid is allowed to flow down into a receiving container before flowing to the expansion valve.

When the liquid flows through the expansion valve, it enters the region of low pressure. This pressure change causes the liquid to expand and vaporize into the evaporator, which is a long metal tube wrapped around the chamber containing the material that is being made cold.

Industrial Refrigeration Systems (continued)

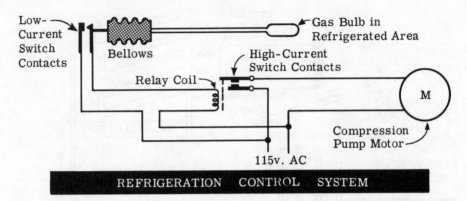

REFRIGERATION CONTROL SYSTEM

The evaporator is also essentially a heat exchanger, although its form may be somewhat different from that of the condenser. In large refrigeration chambers, the evaporator is sometimes in approximately the shape of an automobile radiator, and the air in the chamber is cooled by an electric fan that circulates it between the coils of the evaporator. In plants where ice is made, and in large refrigerated warehouses, the evaporator is immersed in a tank of salt water ("brine"). Then the cold brine is circulated around the material to be frozen.

The electrical control arrangement for any refrigeration system is quite simple. The diagram shows a generalized control system that is suitable for most refrigeration installations. A temperature-sensitive switch is the heart of the control system. The switch can be any of the types described earlier, but one of the most popular is the gas bulb and bellows type shown in the diagram. When the temperature in the refrigerated chamber, or in the circulating cold brine, rises above the desired level, the gas in the bulb expands sufficiently to enable the bellows to close the switch. In small installations, the switch closes the circuit to the electric motor that drives the compression pump. In large installations, where large electric motors are used, the switch energizes the starting relay in a motor controller.

Once the compression pump motor is started, it continues to operate until the temperature in the refrigerated chamber is back down at the desired level. At that time the gas in the switch bulb has decreased in volume by an amount that is sufficient to cause the switch bellows to contract and open the switch contacts. Now the compression pump motor stops, and the system remains shut off until the temperature in the refrigerated chamber again rises above the desired level.

The closing of the temperature-sensitive switch also operates any auxiliary devices in the refrigeration system. These include fans to circulate cold air within the refrigerated chamber; blowers to force cooling air through the condenser, or electric control valves or circulator pumps to start the flow of cooling water over the condenser; and circulator pumps to force the flow of cold brine over the containers of material that are to be made cold.

Industrial Air Conditioning

Many people have the somewhat mistaken idea that air conditioning is simply the process of circulating cooled air through a building in order to make it comfortable during hot weather. Although cooling the air is an important part of air conditioning, this is not all that is involved. In most industrial applications, air conditioning includes controlling the temperature, humidity and amount of circulation of the air in the building. In other industrial applications, air conditioning also includes the removal of pollen, dust, bacteria, odor-carrying materials and poisonous or toxic gases from the circulating air. Some systems are designed for use only during the summer, but it is becoming quite common for many industrial plants to use air conditioning systems the year round. In the winter the air is warmed and in the summer the air is cooled; all the other functions that have been mentioned are performed throughout the year. The general technique in air conditioning is to recondition and recirculate already conditioned air and to continuously introduce sufficient outside air and exhaust enough recirculated air to maintain a suitable oxygen level and remove excess carbon dioxide.

In large industrial installations, heating and cooling of the air is accomplished as described in the topics on heating and refrigeration earlier in this section. In other installations, individual offices, laboratories, and special work spaces are each equipped with an individual air conditioner unit which usually provides most of the desirable functions with the exception of heating.

Humidity is a very important factor in determining the physical comfort in a working area. Humidity is usually described in terms of "relative humidity percentage," which is equal to the weight of water vapor actually contained in a cubic foot of air divided by the weight of water vapor that would be contained in a completely saturated cubic foot of air at the same temperature. Investigations have shown that indoor temperatures ranging from 75 to 80 degrees Fahrenheit can be considered comfortable when the relative humidity is between 55 and 45 percent. Comfort can be obtained at higher temperatures with further decrease in humidity, but it is considered more practical to reduce air temperature rather than attempt to decrease relative humidity below 45 percent.

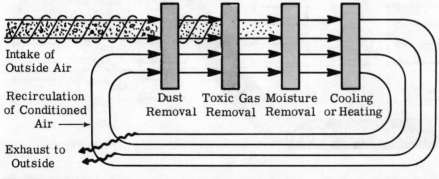

Intake of Outside Air

Recirculation of Conditioned Air ⟶

Exhaust to Outside

Dust Removal Toxic Gas Removal Moisture Removal Cooling or Heating

BASIC PRINCIPLES OF INDUSTRIAL AIR CONDITIONING

Industrial Air Conditioning (continued)

Air can be dehumidified by cooling it to temperatures below those desired and then allowing it to warm up to the desired temperature. The reason for this is that warm air is able to hold more water vapor than cold air. Thus, when air is cooled sufficiently, it cannot hold all the moisture that it previously contained. The excess moisture condenses out in the form of water droplets, and when the temperature of the air rises, the air is highly dehumidified.

Two basic methods are used for dehumidification in industrial installations. In one method, air is forced through a chamber which is filled with a continuous fine spray of cold water. The water is generally cooled by standard refrigeration techniques and is continuously recirculated (unless large volumes of cold water are available from wells or local streams). One advantage of this method is that the water spray washes out many types of solid particles and some toxic materials that may be contained in the air. In the alternate method of dehumidification, the air is forced through a refrigeration system evaporator unit, or through a similar structure through which cold brine is pumped.

Note that dehumidification is generally required only during the summer. During the winter, the outside air is quite cold and normally at low humidity. When this air is heated, its humidity is often much too low for comfort, and is also much too low for certain industrial operations, such as textile manufacture. In such cases the air is usually forced through a spray chamber so that it will be able to absorb some moisture.

While continuous dehumidification and humidification are adequate for most industrial situations during summer and winter, there are some applications in which precise humidity control is required at all times. These are found in some chemical, biological and physics laboratories, and in industrial super-clean "white rooms" in which high-precision manufacture, assembly and testing are conducted.

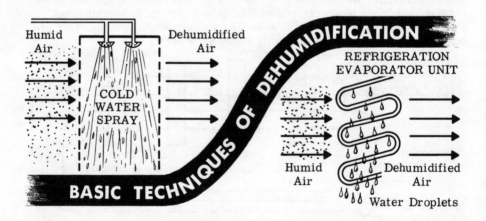

Industrial Air Conditioning (continued)

One of the simplest and most reliable methods of controlling humidity is the fiber hygrostat. The operation of this device depends upon the fact that certain plastic, silk and plant fibers and, particularly, blond human hairs, expand when moist and contract when dry. Several such fibers are installed in a case with slotted sides. One end of the fiber is attached to a fixed point, and the other end is attached to the arm of a lever which has a slight spring tension to resist the expansion and contraction of the fiber. The free end of the lever arm has a tiny electrical contact, and the matching contact is mounted in the case by means of an insulator. The mechanism can be set so that the contacts are closed when the humidity is either above or below the desired level. It is possible to equip the mechanism with two sets of contacts, so that either humidity extreme will close one pair of controls. Contact closure energizes a relay coil which starts the operation of humidification or dehumidification equipment.

Once temperature and humidity control are achieved, the final problem in air conditioning is the removal of dust and toxic gases from the air. Spray-type humidifiers can be used to remove much of the dust, but these are not always used and are not always sufficiently effective.

Filters provide an effective and economical means for removing small solid particles from the air. The simplest type of filter is a large flat unit that is placed in the air stream. The unit consists of a metal screen that contains a tightly packed mat of plant, plastic or glass fibers. As the air passes between the closely intermeshed fibers, the solid particles are trapped, and the cleaned air passes through. The disadvantage of this type of filter is that once many dust particles have been trapped, the spaces between the fibers are filled, and air circulation is highly impeded. Frequent installation of new filters is thus necessary.

An alternate type of filter is one which contains closely packed oil-coated metal strands. The dust adheres to the oil; and the filter can be removed, cleaned, recoated with oil and used again. In extremely dusty areas, an electric motor drive system can be used to move a continuous band of such filter material in the path of the air stream while other parts of the band are being cleaned and recoated with oil.

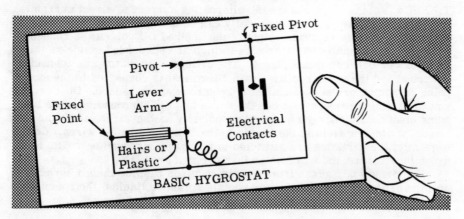

BASIC HYGROSTAT

Industrial Air Conditioning (continued)

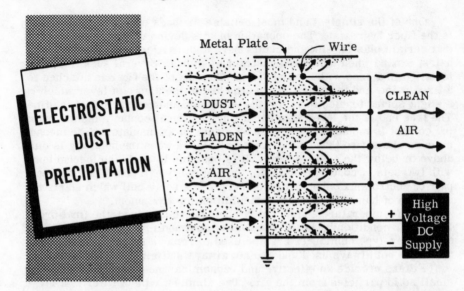

Electrical methods for removing even the smallest particles from the air are also available. The general method is known as "electrostatic precipitation," and the specific techniques vary widely among equipment manufacturers. The method is based upon the fact that dust or smoke particles can be electrically charged by passing them through an electric field. Once the particles are charged, they are attracted out of the air stream by metal surfaces that are oppositely charged. The particles adhere to the metal, from which they are periodically washed or scraped.

The direct-current voltages that are required for this process range from 15,000 to 100,000 volts, depending upon the characteristics of the dust or smoke and upon the volume that must be processed. This voltage is obtained by using a transformer to step up powerline voltage to the desired level and then using "rectifying" techniques (see BASIC ELECTRONICS, Volume 1) to change the alternating current to direct current.

Dust or smoke particles generally can be charged either positively or negatively. The rectifier output of the desired DC polarity is connected to one or more small-diameter wires which are suspended inside metal cylinders or between metal plates. The cylinders or plates are connected to ground and the other rectifier output terminal is connected to the same point, providing protection against a dangerous shock hazard. Dust or smoke particles passing between the wires and the surrounding walls become electrically charged at the same polarity as the wires, since the strongest electric field in the region is that surrounding the wires. Consequently, the particles are attracted to the large surrounding walls, to which they adhere and from which they are removed.

Removing toxic gases from the air requires passing the air through chemical filters. The filters may contain solids or liquids; the specific ingredients depend upon the types of gas that must be removed.

Industrial Liquid and Gas Processing Systems

A large variety of liquid and gas processing systems are in use. Thousands of chemical, medical, industrial, and food products require the use of liquid and gas processing systems in their manufacture. Most of these processes are quite different from each other and most involve highly complex physical and chemical functions which can be fully appreciated only by process engineers and chemists. Instead of attempting to summarize the physical and chemical processes that are involved in this large field, this topic will present a review of the principles of electrical control that are used in such systems.

Most phases of liquid and gas processing involve some method of controlling the function that is being performed, so that the output product will have the desired characteristics. The most basic method is to have one or more men continuously examine the output product and regulate the flow of input ingredients and the conditions of processing so as to correct any undesirable trends. The accuracy with which the men can control the output product depends mainly upon the speed and accuracy with which they can correct the flow of input ingredients and the processing conditions. Manually controlling such processes is largely obsolete, and automatic control is used wherever it is practical.

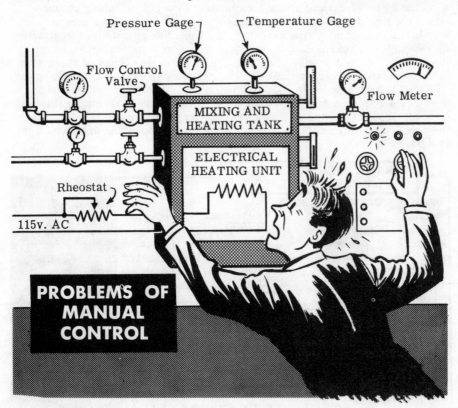

Industrial Liquid and Gas Processing Systems (continued)

All that you have learned about electromechanical control servo systems can be applied to automatically controlled liquid and gas systems. There are slight differences in the terms and in the system connections, but the basic principles are exactly the same as those you studied in the section on Electromechanical Servo Control Systems.

The diagram shows the basic elements of an automatic liquid or gas processing system. It is important to note that the control loop shown is only for the temperature control portion of the process. The complete process may be that of mixing two or more liquids or gases under precisely determined conditions of pressure and temperature. Thus, individual control loops may be required for controlling the volume of each input liquid or gas, the pressure, the temperature, and possibly the rate of mixing. Consequently, a diagram of the complete processing system would show at least five control loops, each of which would look similar to the one that is shown.

Assume that the process is indeed the mixing of liquids and gases under controlled pressure and temperature conditions. Mixing can be performed by a motor-driven paddle in the mixing vessel or by using an electromechanical device to vibrate or rotate the vessel. Heat can be supplied by an electrical resistance heater, by a coil of tubing through which hot liquid or steam is flowing, or by a variety of other means.

In the control loop that is shown, the transducer could be a resistance thermometer, a thermocouple or any of the other temperature-measuring devices that were discussed in the previous sections. Some of these may have associated amplifier units to raise transducer signals to usable levels. The type selected depends upon the operating temperature range and the designer's requirements for either on-off or proportional temperature control. In addition, the temperature transducer may be inserted in either the processing unit or in the product output line, depending upon which it is desired to control.

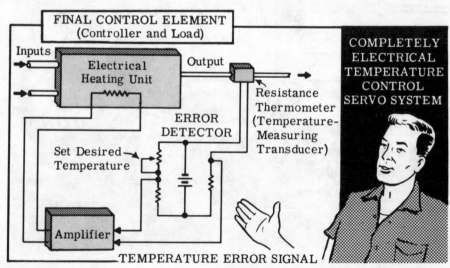

FINAL CONTROL ELEMENT (Controller and Load)

Inputs

Electrical Heating Unit

Output

Resistance Thermometer (Temperature-Measuring Transducer)

ERROR DETECTOR

Set Desired Temperature

Amplifier

COMPLETELY ELECTRICAL TEMPERATURE CONTROL SERVO SYSTEM

TEMPERATURE ERROR SIGNAL

Industrial Liquid and Gas Processing Systems (continued)

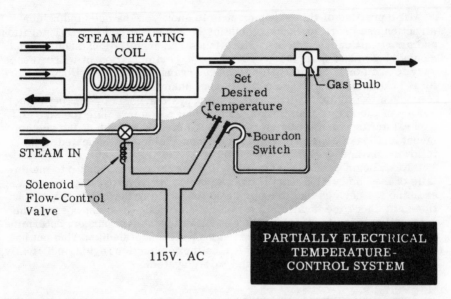

STEAM HEATING COIL

Set Desired Temperature

Gas Bulb

Bourdon Switch

STEAM IN

Solenoid Flow-Control Valve

115V. AC

PARTIALLY ELECTRICAL TEMPERATURE-CONTROL SYSTEM

The error detector can be any one of the types that were considered in the section on Electromechanical Servo Control Systems. Its purpose is to receive the electrical signal from the temperature-measuring transducer, to compare it with the desired temperature condition, and to produce an output signal that is proportional to the difference between the actual condition and the desired condition. This desired condition is usually set into the error detector as a fixed value, although it can be made to be a variable value, as you learned in Servo Control Systems.

In liquid and gas control systems, the controller and the load can be any of the devices you learned about previously. However, one factor that should not be misunderstood is that part or all of the controller and the load are often constructed as one unit. One example is a solenoid valve in which the solenoid is the controller and the portion of the valve that closes or opens the fluid passage is the load. In automatic process control systems, such a device is known as the "final control element."

Another point that should not cause confusion is that a portion of the controller and transducer may be constructed into the error detector unit. The thermostat is a familiar example of such a device. Its bi-metallic element is a transducer which changes temperature to mechanical motion that closes the switch elements. Another example that is not so familiar is a Bourdon gage whose moving element closes a switch, adjusts a potentiometer, or adjusts the valve in a compressed air line that is used to drive another valve element.

There are many process control devices which may contain several portions of the servo control system. If you remember that every servo system must have an error detector, a controller and a load, you will be able to locate where these functions are performed in the system.

Experiment - Industrial Fluid Control Systems

The purpose of this experiment is to show you the outstanding construction and operating characteristics of industrial heating, refrigeration
and air conditioning systems. Since industrial installations such as these
cannot be brought into places of study or experimentation, it will be necessary for you or your instructor to make arrangements to visit one or more
local industrial plants equipped with such installations.

When examining an industrial heating system, begin by making a quick
survey of the entire installation, so that you will appreciate the size and
general arrangement of the system. Make a rough sketch of the system
layout and make separate diagrams to show the details indicated in the
following paragraphs.

Next, begin over again by examining the furnace. Check into the details of the combustion unit; learn whether it burns coal, coke, oil or gas;
examine the devices that are employed for bringing the fuel to the combustion unit; check the details of the control and safety system; observe the
combustion unit in operation. Now examine the heat exchanger; determine
whether it uses water, steam or air as an exchange medium; find out how
the exchange medium enters and leaves the combustion region; and, finally,
check the details of the control and safety system.

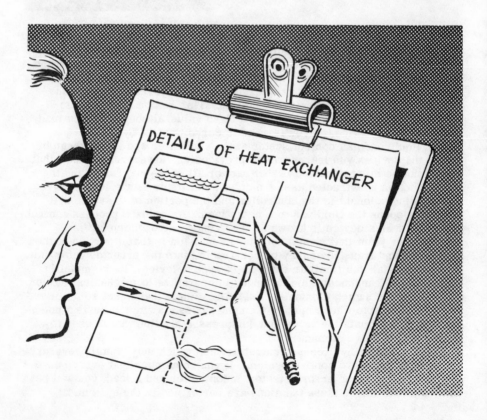

Experiment - Industrial Fluid Control Systems (continued)

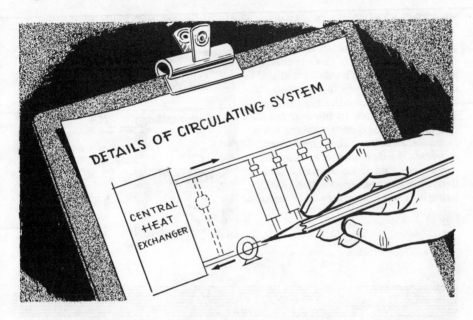

When examining the details of the heating system circulation provisions, begin by observing the arrangements for driving the fluid through the system. Next, locate and identify the major and minor ducts or pipes that carry the heat exchanging fluid to the local heat exchangers and back to the furnace. Also examine the details of the local heat exchangers. To complete your study of the heating system, examine the details of the control system, and then observe the complete temperature control cycle by raising and lowering the setting of one of the local thermostats.

Follow the same general procedures in making your survey of an industrial refrigeration system. Make a sketch of the system layout showing all major components. Locate and identify the compressor, condenser, expansion valve, and evaporator. Check any arrangements, such as fans or cold brine circulation systems, for cooling areas distant from the evaporator. Finally, examine the thermostat and control system and raise and lower the setting of the thermostat so that you can observe the starting and stopping cycle of the system.

Procedures similar to those used with the heating and refrigeration systems can also be used in examining an industrial air conditioning system. Make a layout diagram showing the location of all the major components in the system. Locate and identify the provisions for heating and cooling the air in the building. Next, examine the details of the arrangements for dehumidifying the air and any control system for continuously monitoring or adjusting air humidity. Identify the various components of the filtering system, and, finally, examine the control system and observe it in operation.

Review of Industrial Fluid Control Systems

HEATING SYSTEMS - In a typical system, the furnace contains a combustion unit which burns a fuel, and a central heat exchanger which conducts the fluid to be heated to the vicinity of the burning fuel. The circulating system moves the heated fluid to local heat exchangers in the areas to be heated, and then the cooled fluid is circulated back to the central heat exchanger. A control system maintains safe fuel burning conditions, prevents the development of excessive pressures and temperatures, and provides the required local heating exactly when and where it is needed.

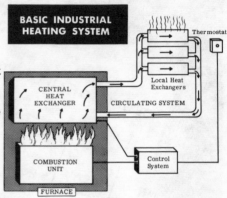

BASIC INDUSTRIAL HEATING SYSTEM

Thermostat

Local Heat Exchangers

CIRCULATING SYSTEM

CENTRAL HEAT EXCHANGER

COMBUSTION UNIT

Control System

FURNACE

REFRIGERATION SYSTEMS - In a typical industrial vapor-compression refrigeration system, a pump compresses a gas into a condenser, where the gas is liquefied and loses heat. The cooled liquid is forced through a small valve opening into an evaporator, where it expands to the form of a gas and absorbs heat. A temperature-sensitive switch turns the pump motor on and off to maintain the desired stable temperature.

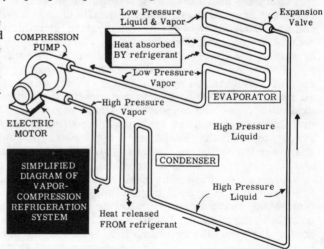

COMPRESSION PUMP

ELECTRIC MOTOR

SIMPLIFIED DIAGRAM OF VAPOR-COMPRESSION REFRIGERATION SYSTEM

Low Pressure Liquid & Vapor

Expansion Valve

Heat absorbed BY refrigerant

Low Pressure Vapor

High Pressure Vapor

EVAPORATOR

High Pressure Liquid

CONDENSER

High Pressure Liquid

Heat released FROM refrigerant

Review of Industrial Fluid Control Systems (continued)

AIR CONDITIONING - A complete air conditioning system controls the temperature, humidity, circulation and obnoxious-material content of the air in the building.

Heating and cooling methods have been described. Air is dehumidified by cooling it to condense out the water vapor. Chemical filters are used to remove toxic gases, and mechanical filters are commonly employed for removing solid particles.

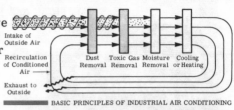

Intake of Outside Air

Recirculation of Conditioned Air

Exhaust to Outside

Dust Removal Toxic Gas Removal Moisture Removal Cooling or Heating

BASIC PRINCIPLES OF INDUSTRIAL AIR CONDITIONING

In electrostatic precipitation, solid particles are charged by passing them through an electric field and they are then attracted out of the air by oppositely charged surfaces.

LIQUID AND GAS PROCESSING SYSTEMS - Individual servo loops control each vital characteristic of system operation. In each loop, a transducer measures the process characteristic of interest, an error detector produces a signal proportional to the difference between the actual and desired conditions, a controller provides the power for producing the desired change, and a load makes the correction in the process.

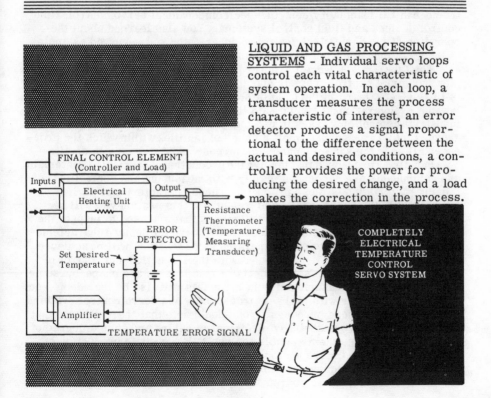

FINAL CONTROL ELEMENT
(Controller and Load)

Inputs

Electrical Heating Unit

Output

Resistance Thermometer
(Temperature-Measuring Transducer)

ERROR DETECTOR

Set Desired Temperature

Amplifier

TEMPERATURE ERROR SIGNAL

COMPLETELY ELECTRICAL TEMPERATURE CONTROL SERVO SYSTEM

Introduction

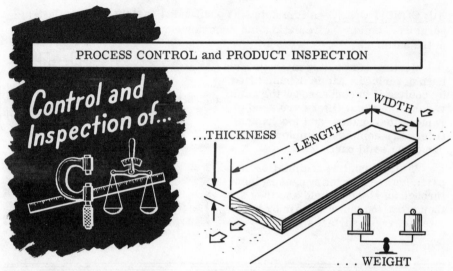

In Sections 4, 5, 6, and 7 you learned the basic fundamentals of electromechanical machinery control, electromechanical servo control, fluid control devices and fluid control systems. You also learned about the operation of the basic electrical transducers, and you reviewed examples of the ways they are used in typical industrial systems.

The fact that you were introduced to many different and fairly complex industrial control systems should not lead you to believe that there is little else to learn in the field of electrical industrial process control. Without exaggeration, it can be said that there are thousands of different industrial control processes in use today. Fortunately, these can be grouped into a reasonably small number of families within which the processes all have the same fundamental purpose and differ only in detail.

Industrial processes that involve the production of fabricated materials and components are concerned mainly with measuring and controlling certain characteristics of those products. These characteristics include length, width, thickness, shape and weight. In this section you will be introduced to the basic electrical techniques that are used to inspect the product to determine whether it does indeed have the desired characteristics and, if it does not, to adjust the process so that they will be achieved. Most of the section will be concerned with the inspection and control of processes which produce solid objects of specific size and shape, but some information on the measuring of bulk materials will also be included. You are already familiar with the basic transducers and servo control systems that are used for these purposes. You should note that the techniques that will be reviewed are essentially electrical in nature and have a degree of accuracy that makes them suitable for use in large-scale production of large objects. For the inspection and process control of small or precision parts, the techniques are almost completely electronic in nature, and are the subject of another course.

Product Length Control and Inspection

In the production of rod, tubing, cable, sheets, rails, beams and struc-
tural elements, the product is made in very long or continuous lengths, but
is generally sold in a range of standard lengths. The reason for this is
that most purchasers of such products plan their own production on the
basis of standard lengths, rather than concern themselves with extensive
cutting operations. Because of this, there is mutual agreement in which
the manufacturer supplies the lengths that are in greatest demand and the
purchaser gears his own production to the use of those lengths. Most
manufacturers will supply special lengths at higher prices; the additional
cost decreases as the size of the special order increases.

The most elementary method of producing a standard length of material is to have a human operator use a ruler to measure off the desired
length and then use a tool to cut the material to that length. Although this
technique is widely used in small scale production, it is much too slow
and costly for use in mass production.

One simple method of increasing the speed of this technique is to use
a cutting table. This is a flat bench equipped with a track-mounted cutting
tool, a set of guides, and a stop. The stop is set so that the distance between it and the cutting tool edge is exactly equal to the desired length. In
use, the material is run between the guides until it touches the stop, the
cutting tool is turned on and pushed along its track, and the desired length
is cut. The cut length is removed from the table, and the process is repeated. This method is extremely accurate and flexible. Since the cutting
tool is mounted on a track, its distance from the stop cannot change. The
distance between the stop and the cutting edge can be set with all the accuracy that is required, and this accuracy is maintained until it is changed
by wear in the stop or in the cutting tool edge or track mechanism. No
operator is required to operate the cutting tool, since a complete cycle of
operation is easily mechanized and can be started by having the end of the
material press on a pushbutton switch mounted on the stop surface. The
only real disadvantage of this technique is that a human operator must
adjust the feeding of material onto the table so that its forward motion is
slowed down and stopped before excessive force is exerted against the
stop. The operator's manual adjustment of material feeding slows down
the process, and the electrical control techniques that can be used to replace his judgement will be reviewed in the paragraphs that follow.

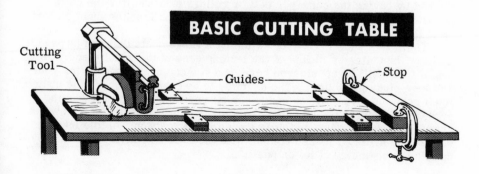

BASIC CUTTING TABLE

Cutting Tool — Guides — Stop

Product Length Control and Inspection (continued)

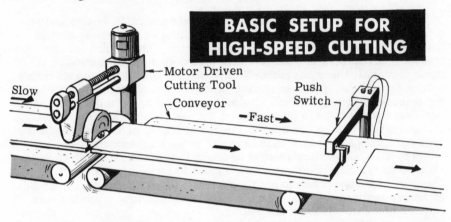

BASIC SETUP FOR HIGH-SPEED CUTTING

Slow

Motor Driven Cutting Tool

Conveyor

Push Switch

Fast

When high-speed processing is desired but extreme accuracy is not required, it is not always necessary to stop the motion of the material in order to cut it to the desired lengths. To accomplish this, the stop in the cutting table is removed and replaced with a simple push switch. The material to be cut is fed at constant speed along the table by means of a conveyor belt or powered rollers built into the table, or by means of some similar device that pushes the material onto the table. When the leading edge of the material reaches the switch, the switch is closed and a high-speed cutter flashes vertically or horizontally through the material. The cutter must be so designed that it will cut so fast that the motion of the material will not cause undesirable length variations and will not damage the cutting tool itself. This is quite practical when the material is soft enough to be cut rapidly or when the length or depth of cut is small.

If the cutting-tool problem can be solved, the only remaining complexity is the design of a suitable switching circuit to activate the cutting tool. The problem in the switching circuit is to devise an arrangement which will start the cutter only when the leading edge of the uncut piece reaches the switch. The cutter must not be activated by the trailing end of the piece that has already been cut. To avoid the complications which might take place if the trailing and leading edges are in contact, it is often necessary to introduce separation between these edges. This is accomplished by having the conveyor belt or rollers located after the cutter position operate at a faster speed than those which feed the uncut material up to the cutter position.

There is a wide variety of switching arrangements that can be used to activate the cutter by means of the leading edge of the uncut piece. Only one of these will be considered here, and you can design others for yourself as a study problem. In the example to be considered here the switch itself contains lower off, on and upper off positions. When the leading edge of the uncut material is approaching the cutting position, the switch arm is all the way down and is in its lower off position. As the leading edge of the material makes contact with the switch arm, the arm is moved up into the beginning of its on position.

Product Length Control and Inspection (continued)

The closing of the switch circuit energizes a relay whose contacts supply voltage to the cutting mechanism. As the material continues to move forward, the switch arm continues to move upward through its on position, and the cutter completes its operation. Further forward motion of the material moves the switch arm higher and the contacts go into their upper off position. They remain in this position as the cut length of material moves under the switch. When the trailing edge passes under the switch arm, the shape of the arm permits it to drop immediately. The construction of the switch permits the contacts to open immediately, so the switch goes from one off position to the other without going through its on position. Thus the cutter is not activated by the trailing edge of the cut material, but only by the leading edge of the uncut material.

If a cutter cannot be designed to cut through the moving material or if greater length precision is required, the motion of the material must be stopped before cutting takes place. This means that the leading edge of the material to be cut must be made to stop exactly at the stop position. If the speed of motion and/or the weight of the material to be cut are kept low, a braking system is a simple and reasonably inexpensive device that can be used for cutting precise lengths.

The basic setup for this method is a cutting table with a switch placed at the stop position. The design of the switch can be exactly the same as the one described for the previous method, but the relay that activates it performs additional functions. When the leading edge of the material to be cut approaches the switch, the switch contacts are in their "off" position. As soon as the leading edge presses against the switch arm, the contacts are moved to their "on" position. The contacts supply power to a relay coil, and the closing of the relay supplies power to an electromagnetic clutch and a friction brake. The clutch disengages the conveyor belt or rollers from their driving motor and the friction brake grasps the material to stop its motion.

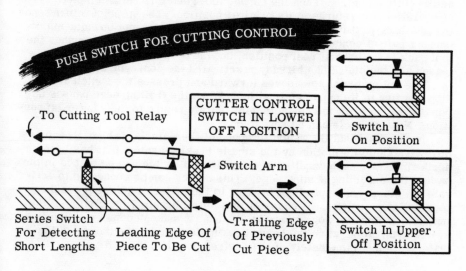

PUSH SWITCH FOR CUTTING CONTROL

To Cutting Tool Relay

CUTTER CONTROL SWITCH IN LOWER OFF POSITION

Switch Arm

Series Switch For Detecting Short Lengths

Leading Edge Of Piece To Be Cut

Trailing Edge Of Previously Cut Piece

Switch In On Position

Switch In Upper Off Position

Product Length Control and Inspection (continued)

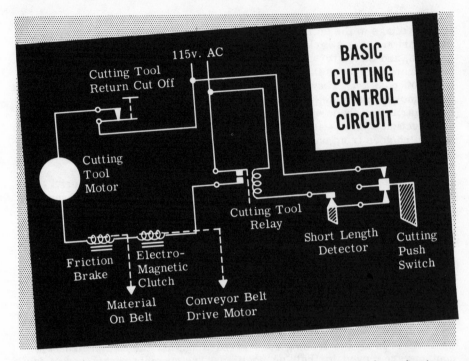

The relay contacts also supply voltage to the cutting tool mechanism. Cutting does not start instantly, since the mechanism must move the tool up to the work before cutting can start. This time interval is adjusted to a length that will assure that the material comes to a complete stop before actual cutting begins. Then the cutting tool goes through a complete cycle of operation and returns to its original position. The speed of return sends the tool back past its normal resting position, and this motion momentarily opens a pair of contacts in series with the relay coil. A spring pushes the tool back to its normal rest position, but the brake has already been released and the clutch has already reactivated the conveyor system.

The cut material now moves forward and presses the switch at the stop position to its upper off position. When the trailing edge passes under the switch arm, the contacts immediately return to their lower off position. Now the cycle can be repeated.

In the event that the weight or speed of the material is high, it becomes difficult to stop its motion by the simple braking system that has been described. Under such conditions, an additional switch can be placed in the path of the oncoming leading edge. This switch can be connected to activate the clutch and apply light braking to the material before it reaches the final stop position. Because of this initial braking, the motion of the material is greatly slowed down by the time it makes contact with the final switch arm. Now, when the heavy braking is applied, the motion of the material stops immediately at the desired position.

Product Length Control and Inspection (continued)

The examples that have been described have assumed the use of a cutting table with a switch at the stop position. This is not absolutely necessary, and adequate cutting control can be achieved by measuring the desired length as the material passes between a measuring roller and a conveyor belt roller. In such an arrangement, the measuring roller is connected to drive a set of precision gears, which in turn drive a wheel that activates the switch. Since the circumference of the rollers and the gear ratios are known, it is a simple matter to construct a switching wheel that makes one complete turn when the desired length of material has passed between the rollers. A stud can be set into the outer edge of the wheel to make a high spot that marks the leading edge of the material.

Thus the passage of the high spot past any fixed reference mark corresponds to the motion of the material leading edge towards the stop position. The high spot can be used to activate a stop switch in the same manner that has been described.

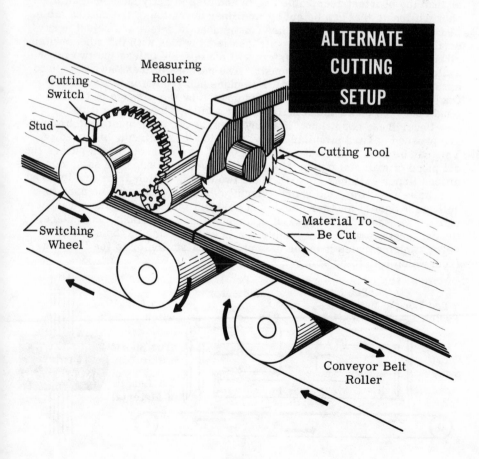

ALTERNATE CUTTING SETUP

Product Length Control and Inspection (continued)

The techniques that have been described have cut the material to a predetermined and measured length. Thus the process can be considered to have performed the functions of both cutting and inspection. However, if additional inspection is required to make sure that the length meets requirements, there are several techniques that can be used.

The usual method of performing inspection is on a "go-no go" basis; that is, the actual measurement of the part is of no real importance. What is important is that the predetermined length be correct to within certain limits. These limits can be between 10 percent too long and 10 percent too short, 5 percent too long and 1 percent too short, 1 inch too long and 0 inch too short, or any other desired limits.

The measurements that are required to determine whether or not the length falls within the predetermined limits can be performed automatically while the part is in motion on a conveyor. This can be accomplished by means of six switches that are arranged as shown in the diagram. The two innermost switches are located a distance apart that is slightly shorter than the shortest acceptable length and also slightly shorter than the shortest length that can be cut by improper operation of the cutting table. (A large number of such switches can be used to detect and reject very small pieces.) Both of these switches are in series with the other switch circuits, and the inspecting system will not operate unless the two inner switches are closed simultaneously. The purpose of these switches is to assure that a length of material is in place and ready for measurement. Once these two switches are pressed upward by the passage of the cut length between them, the remaining four switches are in operation.

Under these conditions, if at any time the two outermost switch arms are pressed upward simultaneously, the "too long" circuit is closed. This can be used to activate a colored light or a solenoid which pushes the cut piece of material onto a "too long" conveyor. Under the same conditions (inner switches closed), if the two center switch arms are lowered simultaneously, the "too short" circuit is closed. This can be used to activate a light of another color or a solenoid which pushes the cut piece onto a "too short" conveyor. If neither of these conditions takes place, the cut length is within acceptable limits and remains on the same conveyor, which carries it to the next processing station or to the location from which it is to be shipped.

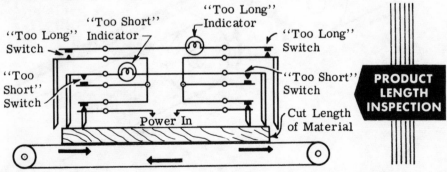

PROCESS CONTROL AND PRODUCT INSPECTION

Product Width and Thickness Control and Inspection

Product width and thickness control and inspection are generally simpler since the difficulties associated with leading and trailing edges are not usually present. The reason for this is that rods, sheets, beams, etc. are generally manufactured in extremely long lengths, and it is a simple matter to turn off the control and inspection system after the passage of each long length over the conveyor.

There is little chance for product width or thickness to vary beyond the desired limits because these dimensions are controlled by pressing the product between fixed walls or rollers, or by cutting it between fixed cutter edges. In either case, the width or thickness can change only when the fixed walls or cutters become damaged, displaced or worn, or when the product is deformed or too narrow before it enters the width-determining mechanism. To avoid constant repetition in the discussion that follows, reference will be made only to width control and inspection, but all that is said also applies to thickness control and inspection.

In cases where width is controlled by means of a fixed mechanism, it is only necessary to inspect the product to make sure that it stays within the required width limits. Such inspection can be performed by switches on a "go-no go" basis. As the product moves along a conveyor, it passes between a fixed roller and a spring-loaded roller which keeps it pressed against the fixed roller. Two normally open switches are located near the spring-loaded roller. The "too narrow" switch has an arm which presses against the moving product edge; if the product becomes narrower, the arm moves towards the fixed roller, and the contacts close. The "too wide" switch also has an arm which presses against the moving product edge; if the product becomes wider, the arm moves away from the fixed roller, and the contacts close. The closing of the contacts of either switch can be used to set off individual "too wide" or "too narrow" alarms, to set off a common alarm, or to stop the conveyor. In any case, an operator is warned; he makes the necessary adjustments to the width-fixing mechanism and permits the process to continue.

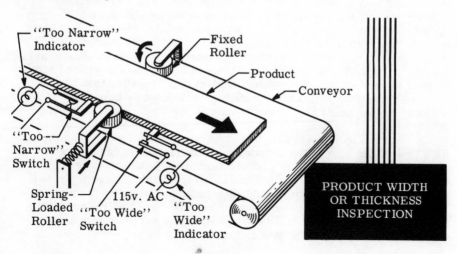

Product Width and Thickness Control and Inspection (continued)

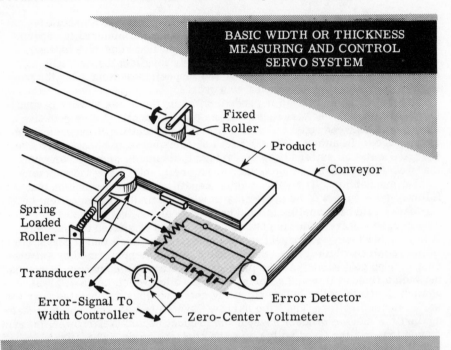

BASIC WIDTH OR THICKNESS
MEASURING AND CONTROL
SERVO SYSTEM

Fixed Roller

Product

Conveyor

Spring Loaded Roller

Transducer

Error-Signal To Width Controller

Error Detector

Zero-Center Voltmeter

Because of the simplicity of this method of measurement, it is an easy matter to obtain direct readings of changes in product width. Such readings can be obtained in terms of fractions of an inch above and below the exact width that is desired. To accomplish this, it is only necessary to position the moving contact of a precision potentiometer against the moving edge so that changes in width change the position of the contact along the resistance element. The voltage changes which are produced by width variations can be read on a zero-center voltmeter that is calibrated directly in terms of fractions of an inch above and below the desired width. When it is necessary to inspect for width changes smaller than can be detected accurately with a potentiometer, it is possible to use any of the physical displacement transducers, such as the strain gage, that were reviewed in Section 5.

If required by the process, this inspection arrangement can be modified to perform as a servo width control system. This can be accomplished by using the output of the potentiometer, strain gage, or other transducer as an error signal. The error signal can be used to drive a servo motor which moves the width-determining cutters or forming walls. The desired input signal is the distance between the fixed roller and the transducer, and the width that is produced by the servo system can be changed at will by adjusting that distance.

Product Weight Control and Inspection

The control and inspection of weight are common examples of industrial process control. Weight control and inspection generally depend upon the use of simple and reliable weighing devices such as the spring and balance scales you have seen in food stores, post offices, railroad depots and airfields. Hydraulic weighing devices are also used. In these, the weight is placed on a platform that is supported by one or more piston-and-cylinder arrangements containing liquid; the pressure that is applied to the liquid is then read on a scale that is calibrated in terms of weight. Regardless of the technique that is used, industrial weighing devices consist of platforms or containers that support the product; pointers and calibrated scales are then used to indicate the weight in standard units.

Industrial weighing devices are frequently equipped with air or hydraulic dashpots which dampen the platform oscillations that occur when material is placed upon a platform. They are sometimes equipped with electromechanical locking devices to hold the platform in a locked position while material is placed upon or removed from it. This also helps to prevent platform oscillation. It is important to prevent platform up-and-down oscillation because an accurate weight measurement cannot be made until this motion ceases, and valuable time is lost if you must wait for the platform to come to rest by itself.

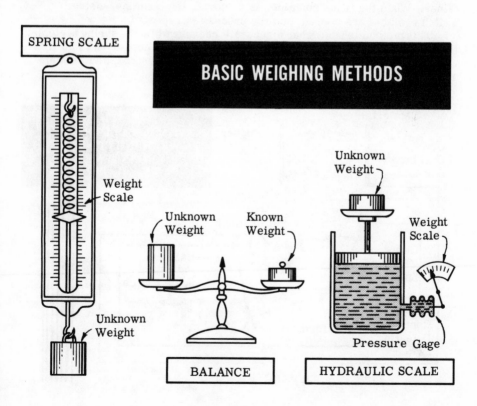

SPRING SCALE

BASIC WEIGHING METHODS

Weight Scale

Unknown Weight

Unknown Weight

Known Weight

Unknown Weight

Weight Scale

Pressure Gage

BALANCE

HYDRAULIC SCALE

Product Weight Control and Inspection (continued)

The illustration shows the basic technique for the electrical control of weight measurement. Before the process begins there is no container on the platform. There are open contacts on the sensitive container-detecting switch next to the platform; the circuit is de-energized and a spring holds the hopper gate in the closed position. When a container is placed on the platform, the container-detecting switch contacts are closed. Now the gate-opening solenoid is energized through the closed contacts of the container-detecting switch and the switch on the balance-indicating scale. The energized solenoid pulls the hopper gate to its open position, and product material begins to fall into the container. Remember, when large amounts of current are required by the solenoid, the scale switch contacts can be connected in series with a relay coil; the relay contacts can then supply the required current to the solenoid.

As the material continues to flow, the weighing platform is gradually pressed down, and the balance-indicating pointer moves across the scale towards the switch. When the pointer touches the switch, the contacts are opened. Now the solenoid is de-energized, and the gate-closing spring quickly pushes the hopper gate to the closed position. By allowing for the weight of the container and placing the balance-indicating scale switch at the desired weight, the proper amount of material is deposited in the container. When the filled container is removed, the container-detecting switch contacts are opened, and the process is repeated.

This method is somewhat inaccurate because while the spring is closing the hopper gate, additional material flows out of the hopper and into the container. This brings the total weight above that desired, and in some applications this is highly undesirable.

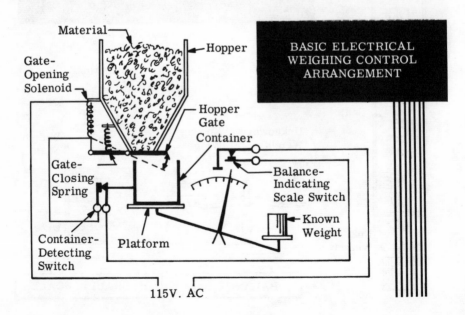

BASIC ELECTRICAL
WEIGHING CONTROL
ARRANGEMENT

Product Weight Control and Inspection (continued)

The simplest way to reduce weight error is to reduce the size of the hopper opening, so that less material flows out while the hopper gate is closing. This technique reduces the error but it also increases the weighing time in the same proportion, and this also may be undesirable.

Another method of reducing weighing error is to carefully measure the amount of extra material that is deposited in the container. Then by setting the balance-indicating switch to a weight that is lower by that amount, the weight of product material deposited in the container can be made very close to the desired amount. The disadvantage of this technique is that there are variations in material flow through the hopper opening, due to changes in particle size and adhesive qualities. These variations may slow the flow of extra material during the closing of the hopper gate, and too little material will be deposited. In many applications, dispensing too little material is just as undesirable as too much.

There are electrical methods for assuring that accurate weights are deposited in the container. The diagram shows one electrical method which permits fast and accurate product dispensing into the container. The arrangement is almost identical to the hopper and switch setup reviewed previously. An important difference is that the hopper has two discharge gates, one large and one small. When the container is placed on the platform, the container-detecting switch contacts are closed. Both hopper gates are opened, and material rapidly flows into the container. The platform is pressed downward by the increasing weight and the pointer moves towards the two pairs of contacts of the balance-indicating switch. When the weight in the container is only a small amount less than desired, the pointer touches and opens the first contacts of the balance-indicating switch. This de-energizes the solenoid which closes the large hopper gate, and most of the material flow is quickly cut off. Now material flows only through the small hopper opening, and the weight increases at a much slower rate. When the pointer touches and opens the second switch contacts, the small hopper gate is also closed. Thus, by using two hopper gates in this manner, the advantages of fast flow and early gate closing have been combined with those of slow flow and at-the-mark gate closing. This technique eliminates the possibility of delivering too little material and also reduces the amount of extra material to a minimum.

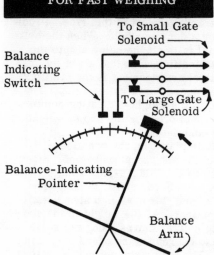

MODIFIED GATE CONTROL
FOR FAST WEIGHING

To Small Gate Solenoid

Balance Indicating Switch

To Large Gate Solenoid

Balance-Indicating Pointer

Balance Arm

Product Weight Control and Inspection (continued)

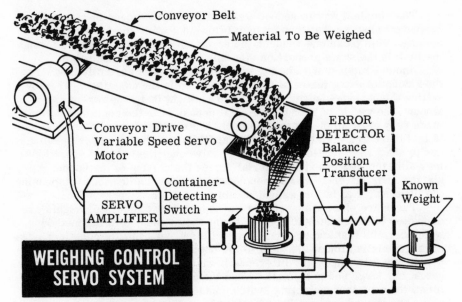

The two-gate hopper setup can dispense product material with a speed and accuracy that is sufficient for most normal applications. It can also be modified for weighing liquids simply by replacing the hopper with a tank or liquid-carrying pipe and by replacing the hopper gates with solenoid-controlled valves.

When extreme weighing speed and accuracy are required, an automatic control system which uses servo techniques provides the best solution. The illustration shows a simple arrangement of this type. Product material is delivered to the container by a conveyor belt. When the belt passes over the final roller, the material falls off the belt and into the container. A funnel-like device can be used to assure that all of the material falls into the container. The control arrangement is the familiar potentiometer (transducer) and variable-speed servo motor setup. The potentiometer control arm is connected to the weight-indicating pointer, and its output is the error signal. The input order is the known weight placed on the balance arm opposite the container.

When the container is set on the scale platform, the container-detecting switch contacts are closed and circuit operation begins. Since the potentiometer sliding arm connected to the balance-indicating pointer is far from the balance position, a maximum error signal is developed. The servo motor, driven by this error signal, turns at high speed, and material is rapidly deposited in the container. As the weight in the container increases, the balance-indicating pointer moves along the scale. This decreases the error signal and also decreases the speed with which material is delivered to the container. The motor stops when the potentiometer arm reaches the balance position, where the error signal equals zero. No more material is deposited in the container.

Product Weight Control and Inspection (continued)

In industrial weight inspection, it is easy to determine the number of pounds and ounces (kilograms and grams) in a fabricated product or in a package of product material. Knowing the exact weight is generally less important than being able to select the units which fall within acceptable weight limits and to sort out those which are too heavy and too light. The diagram shows one basic arrangement for inspecting and sorting objects or containers for proper weight. Dozens of variations are possible, but the principles are based upon the example illustrated.

The operation of this arrangement is based upon the use of a weighing platform and an indicating scale equipped with pointer-actuated switches. A conveyor belt brings the package up to the weighing platform. A small chute may be necessary to place the package on the platform and completely remove it from any contact with the conveyor belt. Notice that the weighing platform is equipped with a locking device that is activated by a spring and solenoid. The platform has an arm with a V-shaped cutout. The spring keeps the locking device pressed into the cutout, and this forces the platform to level at the exact point to which the desired amount of weight would depress it. When the unit to be weighed slides onto the platform, the package-detecting switch contacts are closed. This energizes the solenoid, which pulls out the locking device against the force of the spring, allowing the object to be weighed. When the package is removed from the platform, the contacts of the package-detecting switch open, causing the locking device spring to recenter and relock the platform.

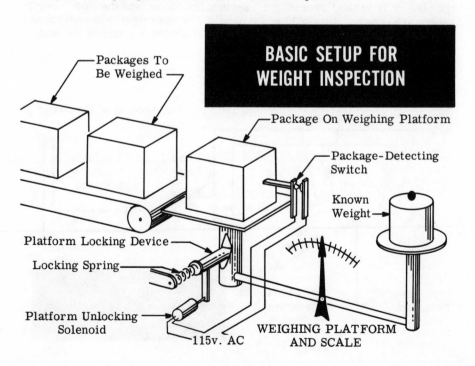

BASIC SETUP FOR WEIGHT INSPECTION

Packages To Be Weighed

Package On Weighing Platform

Package-Detecting Switch

Known Weight

Platform Locking Device

Locking Spring

Platform Unlocking Solenoid

115v. AC

WEIGHING PLATFORM AND SCALE

Product Weight Control and Inspection (continued)

There is one important advantage to this platform locking and center-
ing arrangement. Platform oscillation is reduced to a minimum when an
object is placed upon it. Not only does the lock eliminate the shock of the
object being placed upon the platform, but it also holds the platform at the
exact level at which a unit of the desired weight will balance it. Since it
can be expected that most of the units that are placed upon the platform
will be very close to the desired weight, there will be practically no oscillation at all. This prevents repeated opening and closing of a balance-
indicating switch and shortens weighing time.

The diagram shows a circuit for weight inspection and sorting. When
the package that is to be weighed slides onto the weighing platform, the
platform is unlocked as described previously. The current that energizes
the solenoid also energizes the coil of a time-delay relay. The relay de-
lays the application of voltage to the weight-detecting scale switches for a
period of a fraction of a second to one second, as required. This allows
any platform oscillations to dampen out, so that the wrong scale switch
will not be contacted during such oscillation. Thus, voltage is not applied
to the scale switches until after the pointer has come to rest.

There are three possible positions for the pointer after it has come to
rest and after voltage is applied to the weight-detecting scale switches. If
the pointer is in the acceptable region, the contacts of both scale switches
are closed. Both selection solenoids are energized, and their combined
action pushes the object straight forward onto an "accept" conveyor. If
the pointer is in the "overweight" region, the contacts of the "overweight"
switch are opened. Now only one solenoid ("underweight") is energized,
and the resulting operation pushes the object diagonally across the platform onto an "overweight" conveyor.

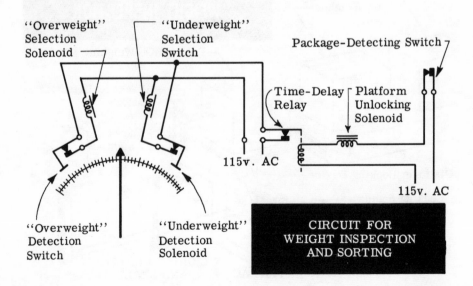

"Overweight" Selection Solenoid — "Underweight" Selection Switch — Package-Detecting Switch

Time-Delay Relay — Platform Unlocking Solenoid

115v. AC

115v. AC

"Overweight" Detection Switch — "Underweight" Detection Solenoid

CIRCUIT FOR
WEIGHT INSPECTION
AND SORTING

Product Weight Control and Inspection (continued)

If the pointer is in the "underweight" region, the contacts of the "underweight" switch are opened. Now the other solenoid is energized, and its operation pushes the object diagonally across the platform in the opposite direction and onto the "underweight" conveyor.

As soon as the unit is off the platform, the package-detecting switch contacts open. Current is removed from all circuits, the locking device levels the platform at its centered position, and the system is ready to repeat its cycle when the next unit slides onto the platform.

In some applications, it may be desired to make a weight inspection of long or continuous strips of material that are being carried along on a conveyor. This can be accomplished as shown in the diagram. The material passes over widely separated supporting rollers so that much of its weight rests on a weighing platform between the supports.

Although the full weight of the suspended material does not rest on the weighing platform, the exact fraction that does can be determined. Then the weighing indicator can be calibrated to read directly in terms of pounds and ounces per linear foot of material.

The indicating scale can be equipped with switches so that "too high" or "too low" alarms will be sounded if the weight of the material varies beyond the desired limits.

Some materials lack sufficient strength for suitably long lengths to be suspended between supporting rollers. Examples of such materials include wet sheets of thick compressed paper, felt, blankets of material made of short fibers, and many types of material that are in early stages of processing before receiving their final strength. The weight of such materials can be measured by making only one modification in the apparatus which was described. This modification is shown in the illustration and consists of placing an endless belt of strong but light material between the suspension points. Now a reasonably long length of the material bears down on the weighing platform. Corrections must be made for the weight of the belt, which is also supported by the weighing platform, but once these are made the system can be made to indicate and operate as described previously.

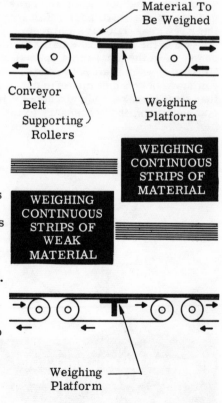

Material To Be Weighed

Conveyor Belt

Supporting Rollers

Weighing Platform

WEIGHING CONTINUOUS STRIPS OF MATERIAL

WEIGHING CONTINUOUS STRIPS OF WEAK MATERIAL

Weighing Platform

Electrical Product Counting

While learning about the previous arrangements for automatic control of product dimension and weight and product inspection, it must have become obvious that a reliable method is required for counting the number of accepted and rejected items. Correct counts are required in order to assure that no fewer and no more than the desired number of items are produced. In addition, for plants which continuously produce standard items, it is necessary to have accurate counts of items produced and rejected. The reason is to assure that suitable quantities of material will be delivered for processing, and to assure that any unusual number of rejects will be discovered quickly so that steps can be taken to make any necessary adjustments in the processing equipment.

Although there is a wide variety of electronic devices available for product counting, electrical techniques are generally based upon a very simple mechanical arrangement. This consists of the setup of gears shown in the diagram. Note that the arrangement consists of identical sets of gears, one large gear and one small gear firmly attached together. These two gears are constructed so that their teeth have matching sizes and shapes, and so that there are ten times as many teeth on the large gear as on the small gear. For example, if the small gear has ten teeth the large gear will have 100 teeth.

When the large and small gears of succeeding pairs are intermeshed as shown in the diagram, a special multiplying effect takes place. To illustrate, when shaft A is rotated one turn, the ten teeth of its small gear can move only ten of the teeth of the large gear on shaft B. The result is that shaft B makes only a tenth of a turn. To cause shaft B to make one complete turn, it is necessary to turn shaft A ten times.

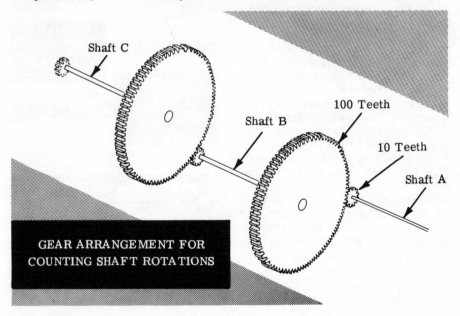

Shaft C

100 Teeth

Shaft B

10 Teeth

Shaft A

GEAR ARRANGEMENT FOR
COUNTING SHAFT ROTATIONS

Electrical Product Counting (continued)

GEAR ARRANGEMENT FOR COUNTING SHAFT ROTATIONS

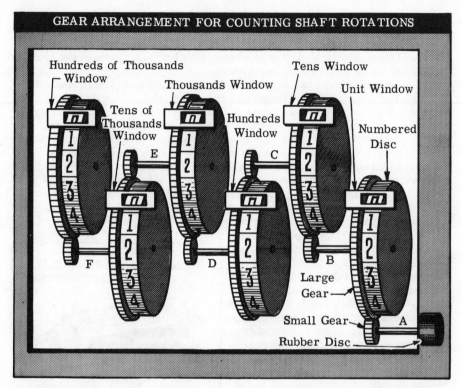

Similarly, to cause shaft C to make one complete turn, it is necessary for shaft B to turn ten times. Consequently, shaft A must be turned 100 times to produce a single rotation of shaft C. Additional pairs of gears can be added, and shaft A will have to be turned 1,000 times, 10,000 times, 100,000, etc. to cause each of these successive shafts to make one complete turn.

This arrangement of gears can easily be converted to a counter that will indicate the number of turns made by a rotating shaft. To accomplish this, it is only necessary to attach to each large gear a disc with the numbers 0 through 9 marked on its edge. Reading of the counter is simplified by adding a slotted plate which exposes only the uppermost number. Thus, one turn of shaft A will cause the large gear on shaft B to move one tenth of a turn - this causes the 0 mark on the attached disc to move away from the uppermost position, and the number 1 will be seen through the window. Five turns of shaft A will cause the number 5 to appear in the window. The addition of more gears with numbered discs, and the extension of the window will provide a turn counter that will indicate any number of shaft revolutions. To use this counter it is only necessary to place a disc of rubber or any high-friction material on the end of shaft A and to press the disc to the center of any rotating shaft. The result will be a count of the total number of turns made in any desired period of time.

Electrical Product Counting (continued)

A practical improvement to this counter can be made by using a more sophisticated assembly of gears which will bring the numbered discs into a side-by-side arrangement. Then a large number of discs can be incorporated into a practical device of compact size which can be reset to zero with a few turns of an added reset knob.

This arrangement can now easily be converted to a device which is suitable for measuring the length of yarn, wire, rod, tubing and other products that are produced in long continuous strips. To make this type of measurement it is only necessary to attach a disc to the end of the counter and press the edge of the disc against the surface of the moving material. If the circumference of the disc is one inch, every inch of material that passes by will cause the shaft to make one turn; the indication on the counter will be a direct reading of the number of inches of material that has passed by the measuring point. By using discs of suitable circumference, the counter can be made to measure in terms of tenths of an inch, feet, yards, or any other desired unit of length.

A most important application of counters is their use in indicating the number of individual product units that have been produced. The counting device that has been described can be modified so that it will advance its readout scale by one unit each time a lever is pressed. The modification is shown in the simplified diagram and consists of removing the input shaft and gear and adding a lever and ten-tooth ratchet arrangement to the first numbered disc. Each push on the lever causes the ratchet to move one tooth. A spring returns the lever to its starting position as soon as the pressure is removed, and a simple flat spring prevents the ratchet from being turned back to its original position during the lever return.

A lever-actuated counter can be used by mounting it beside a conveyor system that moves product units away from fabrication machines and inspection systems. Each product unit that passes the measuring point presses the lever and causes the counter to register one more unit.

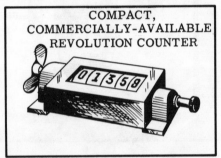

COMPACT, COMMERCIALLY-AVAILABLE REVOLUTION COUNTER

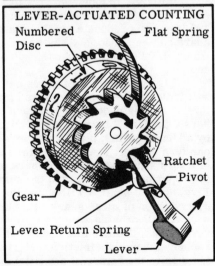

LEVER-ACTUATED COUNTING

Numbered Disc — Flat Spring

Ratchet

Pivot

Gear

Lever Return Spring

Lever

Electrical Product Counting (continued)

Electrical counters are useful when it is desired to have a central display panel which simultaneously indicates important counts that are being made in all parts of a plant. The use of a solenoid and switch contacts is all that is required to convert a lever-type counter into an electrical counter. The solenoid is attached to the lever and pulls the lever each time the switch contacts are closed by the passing product unit. When the switch contacts open in the interval between product units, the solenoid is de-energized, and the spring moves the lever back to its starting position. In this application, only the switch contacts need be mounted next to the product unit conveyor. The counter units can all be mounted on a conveniently located display panel.

A photocell can be used in place of switch contacts for the purpose of activating the solenoid of an electric counter. The diagram shows how this can be accomplished. A beam of light is projected across the conveyor line and strikes a photocell. The photocell generates sufficient current to activate a sensitive relay, or an amplifier unit, which in turn provides sufficient current to drive the counter solenoid. The major advantage of this technique over the use of the simpler switch contacts is that it is more suitable for use with products that are fragile, small, non-uniform in size or shape, or irregularly placed on the conveyor line.

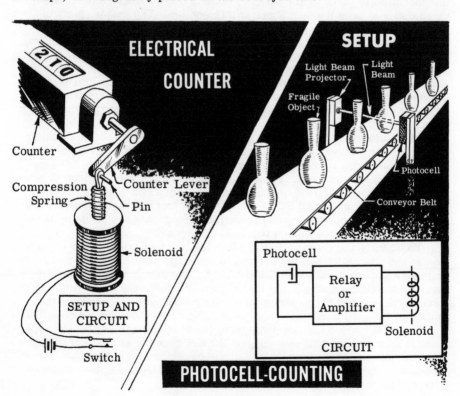

ELECTRICAL COUNTER

210

Counter

Compression Spring

Counter Lever

Pin

Solenoid

SETUP AND CIRCUIT

Switch

SETUP

Light Beam Projector

Light Beam

Fragile Object

Photocell

Conveyor Belt

Photocell

Relay or Amplifier

Solenoid

CIRCUIT

PHOTOCELL-COUNTING

Experiment - Process Control and Product Inspection

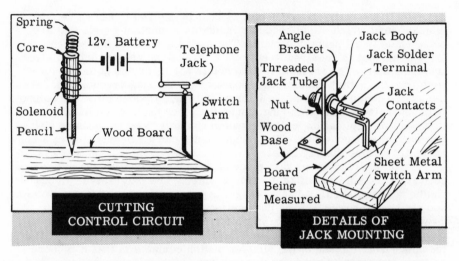

The purpose of this experiment is to give you the opportunity to test the operation of some of the process control and product inspection devices that you have learned about in this section. The major items of equipment required are shown in the diagrams, and the procedures for performing the experiments are described in the paragraphs that follow.

As the first experiment, construct the cutting control circuit shown in the diagram. The circuit is practically identical to the one reviewed earlier, except that a solenoid equipped with a spring and pencil is substituted for the cutting tool, brake and clutch. For simple construction and easy visualization of circuit operation, it is suggested that the switch be made from a telephone jack. These devices are available in constructions almost identical to that shown in the diagram, and the motion of the contacts is very easy to examine. A suitable switch arm can be added by soldering or cementing a bent piece of sheet metal in the location shown in the diagram. The switch can be mounted on a piece of bent sheet metal that is drilled to receive the threaded end of the jack, and fastening is accomplished by means of the nut that is found on the threaded end. Electrical connections to the switch components are made by soldering to the lugs provided on the jack.

To operate the circuit, slowly slide the piece of board along the table toward the switch. When the cut end touches the switch arm, it will first activate and then de-activate the solenoid. The result will be a pencil mark on the board at the place where cutting would take place if a saw were used. Repeat the experiment slowly so that you can examine the motion of the switch contacts and their relationship to solenoid operation.

Move the switch further away from the solenoid and repeat the experiment. You will see that now the pencil mark appears at a longer distance from the cut end of the wood. Repeat the experiment with various distances between the switch and the solenoid, so that you can see that any desired length can be cut.

Experiment - Process Control and Product Inspection (continued)

For the second experiment, construct the product length inspection circuit shown in the diagram. Note that although the diagram shows the various switches at each end of the cut length at different heights and switch arms of different lengths, this is done only to show the operation of the switch contacts. Actually the three switches at each end can be mounted side by side at the same height. Switch arms for opening and closing contacts can be made by soldering or cementing bent pieces of sheet metal, as in the previous experiment.

To operate the circuit, select three pieces of lumber cut to slightly different lengths. Adjust the distance between the switch assemblies so that the piece of average length fits between the switch contacts as shown in the diagram. Now slide the lengths of board along the table under the contacts. You will see that the average-length piece of board will not cause the lamps to light, while the other two pieces will light either the "too long" or "too short" indicator lamps.

As a third experiment, construct the basic product weight control arrangement shown in the diagram. The switches are identical to those used in the second experiment. One is mounted so that it is opened by the balance indicator when it is in the "balance" position. The other switch is closed when a cardboard box is placed on the left platform of the balance. For purposes of simplicity, no automatic hopper is included in the apparatus; you will duplicate the action of the hopper by pouring sand into the box at a slow but steady rate. Do not pour when the light is off; begin pouring when the light goes on and stop the instant it goes off. The weighing cycle starts as soon as the box is placed on the balance, and is over as soon as the light goes off. You will find that you will achieve almost perfect weighing by following the directions indicated by the light.

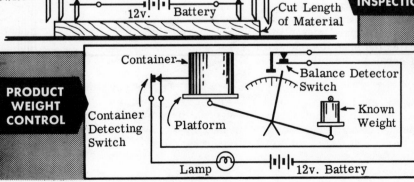

Review of Process Control and Product Inspection

LENGTH CONTROL - Length control involves feeding material past a cutting mechanism, and actuating the mechanism so as to cut off the desired length. Electrical length-cutting control is achieved by using suitably located switches to sense the leading edge of the material and using switch operation to actuate the cutting mechanism.

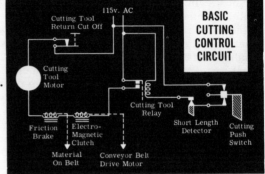

LENGTH INSPECTION - Inspection for proper length is generally on an acceptable or not acceptable (go - no go) basis. Sets of switches sense the leading and trailing ends of cut pieces. Simultaneous actuation of either the "too long" or "too short" switches results in automatic rejection of the piece.

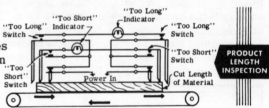

WIDTH AND THICKNESS INSPECTION - Inspection for proper width and thickness is generally on a go - no go basis. Techniques are similar to those of go - no go length inspection, with the exception that a fixed edge eliminates the need for one set of sensing contacts.

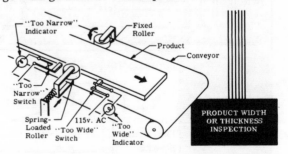

Review of Process Control and Product Inspection (continued)

<u>WIDTH AND THICKNESS MEASUREMENT AND CONTROL</u> - Electrical measurement of width or thickness can be accomplished by passing mate-

rial between a fixed edge and a suitably positioned electromechanical trans-ducer. A zero-center meter indicates width above and below the desired di-mension. Control can be achieved by connecting the transducer into a servo system which adjusts the position of the cutting or forming mechanism.

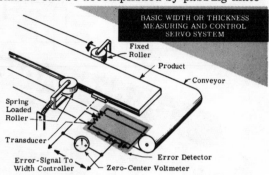

<u>PRODUCT WEIGHT CONTROL</u> - Electrical control of product weighing employs a balance-detection switch or a transducer actuated by a weighing

platform. When the weight is low, the material feed mechanism is actuated. When the desired weight is reached, the feed is stopped.

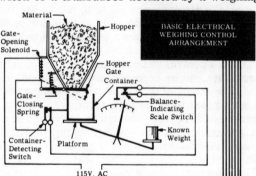

<u>PRODUCT WEIGHT INSPECTION</u> - Inspection is generally on a go - no go basis. The weighing platform is equipped with "underweight" and "over-

weight" detection switches. For products of the desired weight neither switch is closed, and the product is automatically accepted.

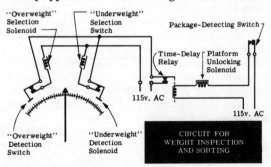

Survey of Remote Monitoring

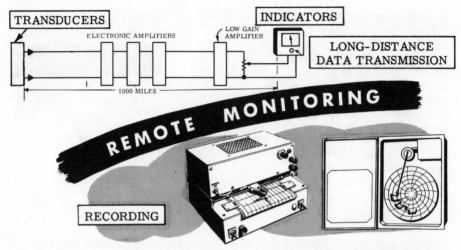

In most of the electrical equipment with which you are familiar, the various indicators are close to where the measurements are being made. However, in large industrial installations, such as chemical or gasoline and oil processing plants, pipeline systems, power generating and distributing plants, metal refineries, etc., it is often necessary (and desirable) to have a central indicator and control panel upon which all important measurements can be remotely monitored and recorded when necessary.

The process of transmitting information over distances, from several hundred feet to thousands of miles, is known as "telemetering." Although measurements are sometimes transmitted over short distances by means of hydraulic and pneumatic techniques, most short-range and all long-range telemetering is accomplished by electrical and electronic techniques. The synchro techniques that were reviewed in Section 5 are examples of telemetering, but are generally restricted to transmission over distances of no more than a few miles.

In the previous sections, you were introduced to a number of devices called transducers, which are used for converting information concerning position, weight, motion, pressure, fluid flow, temperature, etc. to the form of electrical signals. In this section, you will learn of the basic techniques that can be used for transmitting these electrical signals over long distances without loss or distortion of information. You will also find out how these signals can be displayed and permanently recorded in a useful form. As in Section 5, the electronic amplifier will be mentioned, but its operation will not be explained in this course. Again, you must consider the amplifier to be a "black box" into which low-amplitude electrical signals are fed, and out of which come the same signals greatly increased in amplitude and power level.

The telemetering techniques that will be described here are limited to those which your knowledge of electricity will enable you to understand. More complex techniques are also in use, but these require a background knowledge of basic electronics before they can be understood.

Problems of Electrical Signal Transmission

All the electrical transducers you have learned about convert some physical characteristic to the form of a signal consisting of a varying voltage or current. To translate this voltage or current into information concerning the characteristic of interest, it is a simple matter to connect the signal to a suitable electrical meter and to mark the scale of the meter in terms of the desired measurement units.

For example, assume that a tachometer generator and a voltmeter are set up to measure the rotational speed of a motor shaft. When the shaft is not rotating, the voltmeter reads zero; as shaft speed is gradually increased, the voltmeter pointer gradually moves upward on the scale. Exact determinations of shaft speed can be made by purely mechanical techniques. Consequently, the shaft can be rotated over a wide range of known speeds, and for each known speed the voltmeter pointer will position itself at a specific point on the scale. Each of these pointer positions can then be marked with a number that corresponds to the known shaft speed for that position. After that, the tachometer and its voltmeter can be connected to any rotating shaft, and a direct reading of shaft revolutions per minute can be made. Only occasional checks need be made to confirm the accuracy of the reading and to make any necessary adjustments to the scale markings. If extreme accuracy is required and it is desired to make adjustments without re-marking the scale, the calibration can be made with a potentiometer connected between the tachometer and the voltmeter. Thus, for any suitable rotational speed, the potentiometer can be adjusted until the pointer indication corresponds to the known shaft speed.

By using similar techniques, the output of any electrical transducer can be calibrated directly in terms of any appropriate units. The setup is quite simple and straightforward when there is only a short distance between the transducer and its output meter, because the signal losses due to the resistance of the connecting wires are very small and can be compensated in the calibration of the output meter.

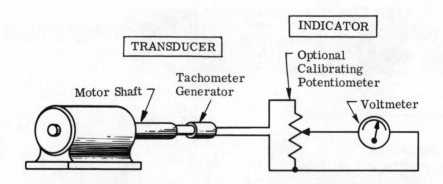

TACHOMETER CALIBRATION SETUP

Problems of Electrical Signal Transmission (continued)

Many problems are introduced, however, when there is a long distance between the transducer and its output meter. Under such conditions, signal losses due to the resistance of the connecting wires are extremely high. By using one or more electronic amplifiers at various points in the connecting wires, it is possible to raise the signal at the output meter to a useful level. However, an arrangement of this type cannot use the described calibration techniques with reliable accuracy because the gain of the amplifiers is not completely stable over long periods of time, and there is the ever-present possibility of long-term and short-term electrical interference that will change the signal level by unknown amounts.

There is a basic and reliable technique for overcoming the difficulties encountered in transmitting electrical measuring signals through very long lengths of wire. It involves the periodic transmission of a reference signal along with the measuring signal of interest.

Assume that it is desired to monitor the speed of a rotating shaft a long distance away. (Any other physical condition could be selected and the techniques would be the same.) The basic technique for measuring shaft speed by electrical means is to attach to the shaft a tachometer that has an electrical output. Then long wires are connected from the tachometer to the calibrating potentiometer and monitoring panel voltmeter. In addition, a suitable number of electronic amplifiers are connected along the path of the wires to assure that the signal reaching the monitoring panel is sufficient to deflect the voltmeter pointer across its full scale when the shaft is turning at maximum speed. For purposes of this example, assume that when the system is set up, the panel meter has a full-scale reading of 10 volts for a shaft speed of 1,000 revolutions per minute and 0 volts for a shaft speed of 0 rpm. Assume also that the system has linear characteristics, so that each volt of scale reading accurately indicates a shaft speed of 100 revolutions per minute. Under these conditions, every marking on the voltmeter scale can be directly converted into terms of shaft speed by multiplying it by 100.

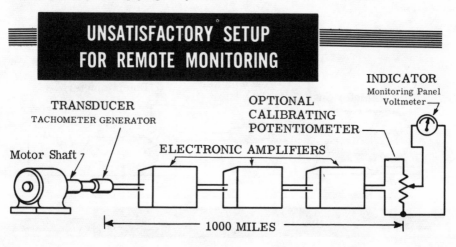

UNSATISFACTORY SETUP FOR REMOTE MONITORING

INDICATOR
Monitoring Panel
Voltmeter

TRANSDUCER
TACHOMETER GENERATOR

OPTIONAL
CALIBRATING
POTENTIOMETER

Motor Shaft

ELECTRONIC AMPLIFIERS

1000 MILES

Problems of Electrical Signal Transmission (continued)

These operating conditions would be completely satisfactory if the amplifier gain were completely stable and if there were no electrical disturbances in the connecting wires. In reality, however, the actual shaft speed may be a constant 1,000 revolutions per minute, but the monitoring meter reading may change from indications of 100 rpm, or lower, to indications that are so high that the pointer is pressed against the upper scale stop. In contrast, the conditions in the amplifiers and in the connecting lines may be completely stable, and it may be actual changes in shaft speed that cause the monitoring meter to change its indications. Under such unstable conditions, it would ordinarily be impossible to interpret the meaning of any changes in monitoring panel meter indications.

The situation can easily be changed from one of no meaning to one of full, accurate meaning by the use of reference signals. This can be accomplished by a few simple modifications, as shown in the diagram. The first modification is to install a switching mechanism near the shaft tachometer. One simple arrangement may be a three-position rotary switch with the switch pole driven by a slow-speed motor and gear mechanism. The tachometer is connected to one of the switch contacts, an accurate source of 10 volts is connected to another of the switch contacts, and the third switch contact is shorted, as shown in the diagram. Thus, as the switch pole slowly rotates, the signal input to the wires is first 0 volts, then 10 volts, and then the tachometer output voltage (example: 5 volts for 500 rpm). This sequence of voltages is slowly and continuously repeated.

At the distant monitoring station, it is known that the transmitting station is transmitting this particular sequence of signals. Now the conditions in the amplifiers and connecting lines are of little significance, so long as these components are capable of transmitting the input signals. Thus, the monitoring panel meter may indicate a series of voltages in slow succession, such as 4, 8, 6, 4, 8, 6, 4, 8, 6, etc. Since it is known that 4 corresponds to 0 revolutions per minute and 8 corresponds to 1,000 revolutions per minute, it requires no great mathematical ability to determine that the distant shaft is turning at 500 revolutions per minute.

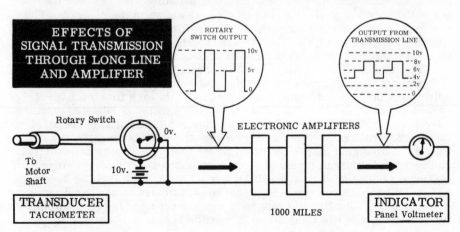

EFFECTS OF SIGNAL TRANSMISSION THROUGH LONG LINE AND AMPLIFIER

ROTARY SWITCH OUTPUT — 10v, 5v, 0

OUTPUT FROM TRANSMISSION LINE — 10v, 8v, 6v, 4v, 2v, 0

Rotary Switch — 0v.

ELECTRONIC AMPLIFIERS

To Motor Shaft — 10v.

TRANSDUCER
TACHOMETER

1000 MILES

INDICATOR
Panel Voltmeter

Problems of Electrical Signal Transmission (continued)

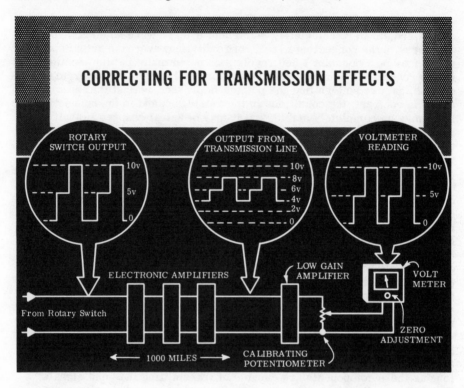

It is also possible to make the panel meter indications read directly in terms of revolutions per minute, in spite of the fact that the voltages reaching it are 4, 8 and 6 instead of 0, 10 and 5. The technique is to connect a low-gain amplifier and a calibrating potentiometer between the output of the connecting wires and the meter, as shown in the diagram. The meter must have a widely adjustable zero setting. The gain of the amplifier must be high enough so that the lowest 10-volt reference signal can be raised to a level of at least 10 volts across the meter terminals.

The method of calibrating the panel meter is quite simple. A series of 0-volt reference signals are carefully observed, and the meter zero adjustment is varied until the meter reads 0 volts each time such a reference signal comes through. Then the potentiometer is adjusted until the 10-volt reference signal results in an indication of 10 volts on the panel meter. Several readjustments may be necessary to obtain these results. Now the third signal that is indicated on the meter, the tachometer signal, can be read directly in terms of shaft revolutions per minute. Before making a reading of shaft speed it is necessary to check that the 0-volt and 10-volt references are being accurately indicated on the panel meter. If not, it is an indication of changes in the connecting wires or the amplifiers, and the described adjustments must be repeated.

Paper Chart Recorders

In many industrial situations it is important to keep permanent records of measurements made by nearby and distant monitoring transducers. Such records are of value while a large industrial system is in normal operation, so that the causes of variations can be localized, and are particularly important when such a system is being placed in operation or when experimental processes are being conducted, so that the effects of various system adjustments can be studied in detail. Commercial electronic instruments, known as "recorders," are available for this purpose. There are a number of different types, but those most widely used all contain the same basic elements: an electronic amplifier, a recording pen, a pen drive unit, a paper chart with suitable graph markings, and a chart drive unit.

The illustration shows the general appearance of two popular recorder arrangements. The paper chart can be circular, or in the form of a wide strip that is unwound from a roller within the cabinet. An electromechanical drive system moves the chart beneath the pen, and the pen leaves a mark on the moving paper.

Incoming electrical signals are amplified and used to drive a meter movement or servo motor. When a meter movement is used, it is often of the zero-center type, and the pen is attached to the end of the pointer. As the incoming electrical signal decreases and increases in amplitude, the pen is moved across the graph paper. The marks thus made on the paper provide a permanent record of the output of the monitoring transducer. The amplifier contains controls for adjusting the amplitude of pen motion, so that the reference signals can be made to correspond to any selected graph marks on the paper chart. This effectively calibrates the pen recording into a direct-reading form, and in terms of any desired measuring units. Even if conditions in the signal-transmitting amplifiers and the connecting wires change, and the amplifier controls are not readjusted, the presence of reference signal markings on the paper chart always provides a standard for measuring the desired signal.

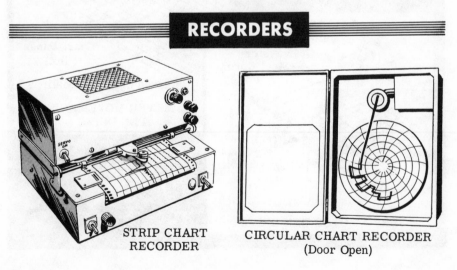

RECORDERS

STRIP CHART
RECORDER

CIRCULAR CHART RECORDER
(Door Open)

Paper Chart Recorders (continued)

Sometimes, particularly in strip chart recorders, a servo motor drive is used instead of a meter movement. In this arrangement, the pen is driven by the servo motor through a gear and pulley system. The pen holder is mounted on a track that spans the full width of the paper, and the pen is pulled back and forth across the paper by means of a steel or silk cord threaded over the pulleys. The arrangement operates according to the principles of the positioning servo system described in Section 5, and the deflection of the pen corresponds to the amplitude of the signal from the monitoring transducer. The advantage of this method over the meter movement method is that it simplifies the mechanical problem of driving the pen across extremely wide paper, and the pen trace appears on rectangular chart markings, a format sometimes considered superior to that provided by most meter movement techniques. The major disadvantage of the servo pen drive is that the pen cannot be moved back and forth as rapidly as it can be deflected by a meter movement, so it is easier to record rapid signal variations by means of a meter movement.

The diagram also shows the graph presentation that is usually traced by a meter-driven pen. Since the meter operates by rotating the pen arm around a pivot, the pen deflections are shown as curved lines, and the graph markings on the paper are generally printed with a corresponding curvature to simplify interpretation.

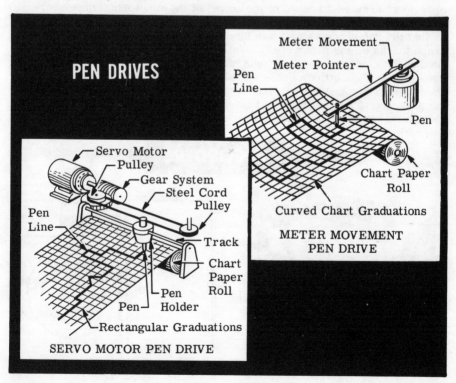

PEN DRIVES

Meter Movement
Meter Pointer
Pen Line
Pen
Chart Paper Roll
Curved Chart Graduations

METER MOVEMENT PEN DRIVE

Servo Motor
Pulley
Gear System
Steel Cord
Pulley
Pen Line
Track
Chart Paper Roll
Pen Holder
Pen
Rectangular Graduations

SERVO MOTOR PEN DRIVE

Paper Chart Recorders (continued)

There are three basic types of recording "pens" in widespread use today. These include the ink pen, stylus and hot-wire types, which will be reviewed briefly in the paragraphs that follow.

Ink pens operate by depositing a line of ink on the moving graph paper. There are many different types of ink pens, ranging from a simple point which holds only a single drop of ink, to ballpoint pens and fountain pens with elaborate reservoirs.

Although ink pens are simple in principle and easy to service, there is always the danger that the pen may clog and the ink may blot. The stylus arrangement eliminates all problems associated with the use of ink. The stylus is a simple cone-shaped piece of steel or synthetic sapphire. Its action can be completely mechanical; that is, its tip can be used to scrape a thin white coating from dark-colored graph paper, thus leaving a dark line on the surface of the paper.

In another type of stylus arrangement, current is passed from a metal tip through an electrically conductive graph paper. The heat of current passage is used to melt or burn away a white coating on dark paper or to cause a chemical action which changes the color of the paper.

A third type of stylus consists of a sapphire point wound with a number of turns of resistance wire. Current supplied through a variable resistor raises the temperature at the point to a level where it melts a thin layer of white wax into dark paper. In another type of chart material, a layer of paper saturated with black wax is covered by a layer of very thin white paper. The heat of the stylus melts the wax below and allows it to saturate the white paper above, thus leaving a black line.

The hot-wire type of recording pen operates according to the same principle as the hot stylus. The important difference is that the wire is about 1/2 inch long, which permits it to be used with a meter movement in the manner shown in the illustration. There is a sharp bend in the chart table; when the hot wire is moved back and forth on the end of the meter pointer, its contact with the paper is limited to the point where the wire touches the bend. Since the wire has length, the meter arm can move through a wide angle without loss of contact between the hot wire and the chart paper. As a result, the recording trace does not have the curvature that otherwise results when a stylus or pen is driven by a meter movement.

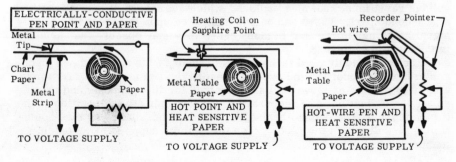

ELECTRICAL RECORDING PENS AND PAPER

ELECTRICALLY-CONDUCTIVE PEN POINT AND PAPER
Metal Tip
Chart Paper
Metal Strip
Paper
TO VOLTAGE SUPPLY

Heating Coil on Sapphire Point
Metal Table
Paper
HOT POINT AND HEAT SENSITIVE PAPER
TO VOLTAGE SUPPLY

Recorder Pointer
Hot wire
Metal Table
Paper
HOT-WIRE PEN AND HEAT SENSITIVE PAPER
TO VOLTAGE SUPPLY

Paper Chart Recorders (continued)

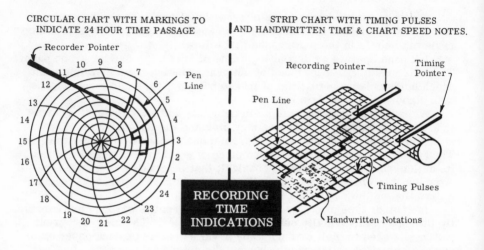

CIRCULAR CHART WITH MARKINGS TO INDICATE 24 HOUR TIME PASSAGE

STRIP CHART WITH TIMING PULSES AND HANDWRITTEN TIME & CHART SPEED NOTES.

RECORDING TIME INDICATIONS

When the time at which electrical signal variations occur is not critical, time markings can be preprinted on the paper chart for use with a specific chart drive speed. When the recording is started, the chart is moved so that an appropriate time marking is under the pen. Circular and drum charts are available with hour markings from 1 through 24, to correspond to the hours of the day. Similar charts are obtainable with hour and minute markings to cover periods of 12 hours or less.

Some paper recording charts, particularly strip charts, are not marked with hours or minutes, but with unidentified markings spaced fractions of an inch or fractions of a centimeter apart. The chart drive mechanism can be set to drive the paper at a reasonably constant known speed. All that is necessary is for the operator to write on the chart the starting time of the recording and the chart drive speed. Then, at any future time, he can determine the time of any point on the recording simply by measuring its distance from the starting line and dividing by the chart drive speed. In some cases, timing must be known to such a high degree of accuracy that calculations based on known chart speed are not exact enough. The most satisfactory method of determining precise time is to record time markings on the chart. This is usually accomplished by means of rapid up and down voltage variations, known as "pulses," which are spaced at known fractions of a second apart. These can be superimposed upon the recording of the signal being monitored, but in many cases they may obscure the variations in the signal of interest.

The most widely used technique is to incorporate a second pen mechanism into the recorder and use it to record the timing pulses. A simple amplifier and meter movement are required for this purpose, and only small pen deflections are necessary to clearly indicate the position of the timing pulses. The pulses themselves can be generated by an electronic timing circuit within the recorder or they can be supplied by an outside master timing system.

Paper Chart Recorders (continued)

In many industrial operations it is necessary to record a number of signals simultaneously. There are two generally used methods for doing this. The first will be described on this page, and the second will be reviewed in the next topic.

The simplest method is to use a separate recorder to record each signal. The obvious disadvantages of this method are that the cost of the recording equipment is quite high, much recorder space is required, a large filing area is necessary to store the chart recordings, and it is quite difficult to examine a number of recordings simultaneously.

Many circular, drum and strip chart recorders are available for tracing out a number of signals on adjacent portions of the same piece of graph paper. Each signal requires its own amplifier and pen drive mechanism, but only one chart and chart drive system is required. If two signals can be recorded simultaneously, the unit is known as a ''two-channel'' recorder; if four signals can be recorded simultaneously, the unit is a ''four-channel'' recorder, etc. Units are available for recording two, four, six and more channels on a single paper chart, and many such recorders can be mounted one above the other in an equipment rack.

Multichannel recorders do not significantly lower the cost of recording equipment. The only cost savings are those that result from the use of only a single cabinet, a single chart drive, and a single timing system for all of the recording channels in one unit. These economies are often more than counterbalanced by the increased cost of the highly compact construction that is required. The real economy is in the saving of installation and chart storage space and in the increased convenience in simultaneously examining a number of different signal recordings.

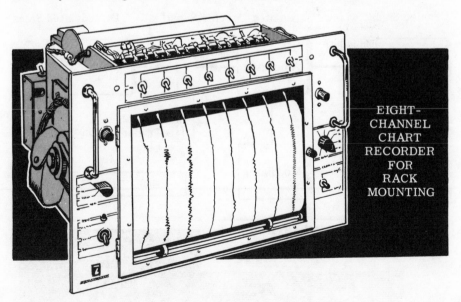

EIGHT-
CHANNEL
CHART
RECORDER
FOR
RACK
MOUNTING

Multiple-Channel Telemetering

In most industrial systems which require telemetering in the first place, it is often necessary to transmit dozens or even hundreds of monitoring signals. While the obvious technique would be to use a different pair of wires to transmit each signal, the installation and maintenance costs of such an arrangement would be prohibitively high. The most common practice is to send a number of signals over the same pair of wires, thereby greatly reducing the total number of wires required. The wires are generally rented from telephone companies and are serviced by those companies. In some instances, the signals are transmitted over power company lines without interference from the electrical power that is also being transmitted through the same wires. The basic techniques used for transmitting multiple signals over a single pair of wires will be reviewed in the paragraphs that follow.

A basic method of transmitting a single monitoring signal over a pair of long lines is to superimpose the signal on an AC signal of higher frequency. The reason for this is that variations in temperature, pressure, shaft speed, and other signals of industrial interest usually occur at very slow rates. For purely electronic reasons, such low-frequency signals are extremely difficult to amplify, while signals at frequencies of hundreds and thousands of cycles per second are much easier to amplify.

There are a number of techniques for superimposing a low-frequency signal upon an AC voltage of higher frequency. The methods that are used and the various results that can be obtained are described in extensive detail in BASIC ELECTRONICS and they cannot be described here.

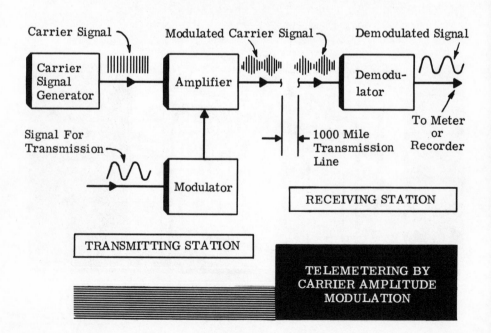

TELEMETERING BY CARRIER AMPLITUDE MODULATION

Multiple-Channel Telemetering (continued)

To satisfy your present interests, the diagram on this page shows the results of one very widely used method known as "carrier amplitude modulation." The high-frequency signal is known as the "carrier," and one of its main purposes is to supply the amplifiers with a signal that is easily amplified. The amplitude of the carrier is varied or "modulated" to correspond to the variations in the low-frequency signal of interest. At the receiving station, the carrier is removed (demodulated), and only the low-frequency signal is fed to the monitoring meter or recorder.

Another important advantage of using carrier signals is that a number of carrier signals can be transmitted at different frequencies over the same pair of wires without intermixing. The situation is similar to the transmission of many radio signals at different carrier frequencies through the space around the earth. A radio receiver can be tuned to one particular frequency, and only the desired signal will be received.

By using similar electronic techniques, a number of different signals can be superimposed upon carriers at different frequencies and then transmitted over the same wires. At the receiving end, each of a number of electronic receivers selects a particular frequency, removes the carrier, and leaves only the signal of interest. You should note the fact that when there is a very long distance between the transmitting and receiving stations, it may be necessary to amplify each carrier a number of times between stations. At each such amplification point, a bank of receiver-amplifiers is necessary. Each unit selects a particular carrier frequency out of the line, amplifies that frequency, and feeds it back into the line.

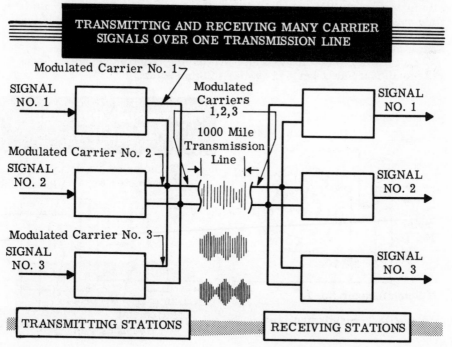

TRANSMITTING AND RECEIVING MANY CARRIER SIGNALS OVER ONE TRANSMISSION LINE

Modulated Carrier No. 1

SIGNAL NO. 1

Modulated Carriers 1,2,3

1000 Mile Transmission Line

SIGNAL NO. 1

Modulated Carrier No. 2

SIGNAL NO. 2

SIGNAL NO. 2

Modulated Carrier No. 3

SIGNAL NO. 3

SIGNAL NO. 3

TRANSMITTING STATIONS   RECEIVING STATIONS

Multiple-Channel Telemetering (continued)

The method of telemetering through the use of a number of different carrier frequencies is most suitable for use in applications where each signal is to be recorded on a separate recorder channel. However, there are a number of applications in which it is desirable to present a number of different signals on the same recording channel.

It is easier to understand this method when similar signals from different sources are being transmitted, but the method can be used with different signals from different sources. To use a familiar example, assume that it is desired to transmit the speeds of ten different rotating shafts over a long distance. In a situation of this type, each shaft is equipped with an identical tachometer, and the output of each tachometer is fed through a potentiometer. The purpose of the potentiometers is to compensate for slight differences in tachometer output, and each potentiometer is adjusted so that its output is equal to that of each of the others when all the shaft speeds are identical. For example, all the potentiometers are adjusted so that their outputs are equal to 10 volts when all the shaft speeds are at 1,000 revolutions per minute.

The signals are transmitted by the same techniques that were previously described for the transmission of calibrating signals. A single-pole 22-position rotating switch can be connected as shown in the diagram. Alternate switch contacts are connected to short-circuit the line, thus providing a 0-volt reference between each tachometer signal and the 10-volt reference signal. Fewer 0-volt references could be provided, but this arrangement nicely separates each tachometer signal from the others, and eliminates possibilities of confusing the identity of tachometer signals. Only one 10-volt reference signal is provided, and that is all that may be required for many applications; more such references can be added by adding more switch positions.

Calibrating, recording and interpreting the received signal sequence is accomplished as described earlier in this section.

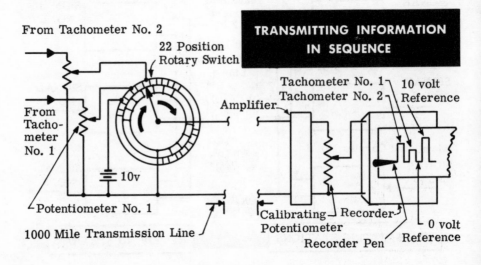

From Tachometer No. 2

22 Position Rotary Switch

TRANSMITTING INFORMATION IN SEQUENCE

From Tacho-meter No. 1

10v

Potentiometer No. 1

1000 Mile Transmission Line

Amplifier

Tachometer No. 1
Tachometer No. 2

10 volt Reference

Calibrating Potentiometer

Recorder

Recorder Pen

0 volt Reference

2-62

Remote Control

Any function that is actuated from a distant location is said to be under "remote control." The distance need not be more than a few feet. The function need only be out of reach from the desired control location.

You are already quite familiar with the concept and details of remote control. The background information is included in many of the previous pages. All that is necessary now is to organize this material into the concept of remote control.

Any circuit which contains a switch can possibly be considered as a simple example of remote control. For example, the most direct method of turning off an electric light would be to remove the lamp from its socket, and turning on the light would be accomplished most directly by replacing the lamp in its socket. Since this technique is inconvenient, it is desirable to achieve remote control by using a switch to open and close the lamp circuit. The switch is usually mounted on the wall close to the entrance of the room and remote lighting control is obtained. Remote control of the same order is provided by any conveniently located switch which is used to turn on a motor, an electromagnet, or any other device.

If you wish to consider that remote control implies that the device being controlled must be completely out of sight and that actuation must be accomplished by more than a simple switch, you are also already familiar with such control circuits. One example is the circuit for controlling lighting by means of the relay system described at the end of Section 3. In this circuit, relay contacts are used to open and close the lamp circuit, and the relay coil can be energized by any number of switches mounted at any desired locations in the plant. By means of such a system, a plant manager or any other authorized person can turn any lights in the building on or off by means of a control panel located in his own office. Similarly, if desired, he can use the same type of circuit arrangement for remotely controlling the operation of the heating and cooling systems or any other equipment in the plant.

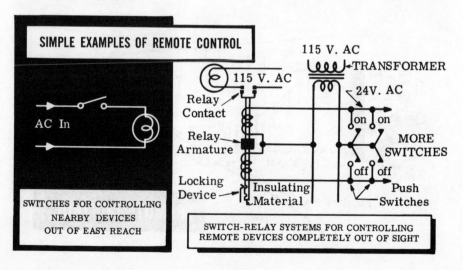

SIMPLE EXAMPLES OF REMOTE CONTROL

115 V. AC

TRANSFORMER

115 V. AC

24V. AC

Relay Contact

AC In

Relay Armature

MORE SWITCHES

on on

off off

Locking Device

Insulating Material

Push Switches

SWITCHES FOR CONTROLLING NEARBY DEVICES OUT OF EASY REACH

SWITCH-RELAY SYSTEMS FOR CONTROLLING REMOTE DEVICES COMPLETELY OUT OF SIGHT

Remote Control (continued)

Your knowledge of remote control circuitry is not limited to simple on-off control. For example, in Section 4, which concerns electromechanical machinery control, you learned about motor controllers that can be used to start, stop, reverse, jog, and control the speed of electric motors. Such controllers can be mounted in any desired location, and complex functions can be accomplished from a remote location.

You are familiar with even more complex remote control devices and systems. In your study of electromechanical servo control systems (Section 5) you learned about a variety of methods for controlling the position of different loads. In any of these systems, the input orders can be adjusted from any desired location, as they also can be remotely adjusted in most of the process control systems described in Section 8.

There are other examples of remote control systems with which you are familiar that are not limited to electromechanical components. Such examples are found in the industrial fluid control systems that you studied in Section 7. In that section you became familiar with the fact that heating, refrigeration, air conditioning, and industrial liquid and gas processing systems can all be controlled from remote locations.

Finally, in the preceding pages of this section, you learned how signals can be transmitted over long distances. These signal-transmission techniques need not be restricted to monitoring what is happening at some distant location. The same techniques can be used to transmit effective control signals - signals for on-off control, speed and motor reversal control, and input order signals for any of the servo systems mentioned earlier. Thus, by means of long-range signal transmission, it is quite a practical matter for an observer to check the operation of a distant system and then adjust the operation of that system to make it perform as desired.

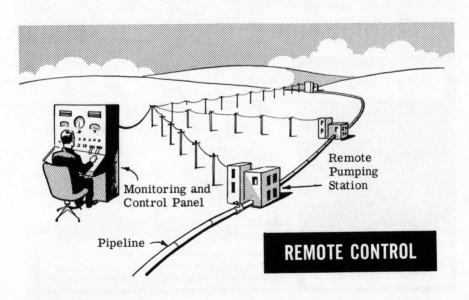

Monitoring and Control Panel

Remote Pumping Station

Pipeline

REMOTE CONTROL

Experiment - Remote Monitoring

In this experiment you will see for yourself the major effects of resistance losses and electrical interference that take place in the transmission of signals through long lines, and the basic methods for correcting
these effects. You will also become familiar with the characteristics of
strip chart recorders. The major items of equipment required are identified in the text and diagrams.

To begin the experiment, you should become familiar with the construction, major features and operating controls of a strip chart recorder.
Because of the many makes and models available, it is impractical to present directions here. The features and operation of the recorder should
first be demonstrated by the instructor, and then he will give you the opportunity to operate the controls for yourself.

The second part of the experiment involves learning the techniques
for calibrating an indicating meter. Make the setup of potentiometers and
meters shown in the diagram. The 12-volt battery and potentiometer on
the left represent any transducer that may be used to transmit a signal over
a line, and the voltmeter connected to that potentiometer provides a means
for indicating the level of the signal that is being transmitted. On the right
are a potentiometer and voltmeter which represent the receiving unit which
is to be calibrated.

To begin the experiment, adjust the transmitter potentiometer so
that the transmitter voltmeter indicates that 10 volts is being sent into the
transmission line. At the receiver end, adjust the potentiometer until the
voltmeter indicates 10 volts; that meter is now calibrated. To prove this,
set the transmitting potentiometer to send any desired voltage into the
transmission line; the receiving meter will indicate the same reading,
within the limits of its accuracy.

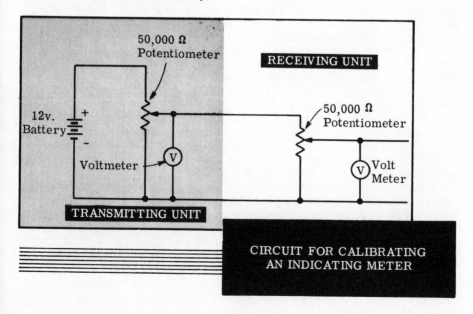

CIRCUIT FOR CALIBRATING
AN INDICATING METER

Experiment - Remote Monitoring (continued)

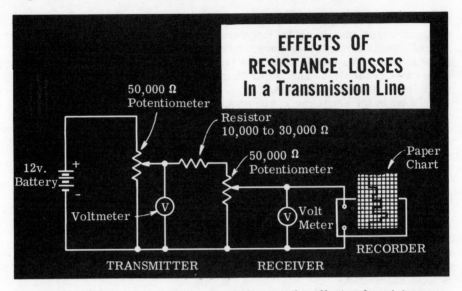

The third part of the experiment indicates the effects of resistance losses in a transmission line, and also shows you how to correct the receiver reading for such losses. To simulate these resistance losses, cut the positive line at its center and connect the cut ends across a resistor with a value between 10,000 and 30,000 ohms. The receiver meter will now read less than the transmitter meter, no matter how you set the receiver potentiometer. Note, however, that you can set the receiver potentiometer so that its meter reads exactly one half. Make this adjustment and see for yourself that no matter how you set the transmitting potentiometer, the receiving meter will indicate one half of that reading, within the limits of its accuracy. Thus, multiplying the receiver meter reading by 2 will produce the value of the signal being transmitted. By the same techniques, you can set the receiver potentiometer so that its meter indicates one fourth, one eighth, one tenth or any other desired fraction of the transmitted voltage.

If it is desired to make the receiver meter indicate the full value of the transmitted voltage, it is necessary to connect amplifiers into the transmission line. This can be simulated, as the fourth part of the experiment, by means of the recorder. The amplifier in the recorder can be used to simulate all of the amplifiers that could be used to correct all the losses in a long transmission line. To do this, connect the recorder across the terminals of the input meter, and place the recorder in operation. Set the transmitted voltage to 10 volts. Now, without readjusting the receiver potentiometer, you can set the recorder for a full-scale pen deflection, which indicates 10 volts. The graph marks on the recorder paper now indicate fractions of that 10-volt maximum. Vary the transmitter potentiometer for any desired voltage, and you will see that the recorder pen deflects to that same voltage.

Experiment - Remote Monitoring (continued)

The final part of the experiment consists of simulating and correcting the combined effects of resistance losses and electrical interference. To do this, make the setup shown in the diagram. Begin the experiment by setting the transmitter switch to the signal position. Adjust the interference potentiometer to any random setting, indicating unknown electrical interference, resistance loss, and loss of zero reference. Adjust the signal potentiometer to any random setting to indicate any particular output that the transducer may be producing. Now start the paper drive and slowly set the transmitter switch back and forth through its three positions. Stop the paper drive and examine the recording. Since the 0-volt and 10-volt reference levels are clearly indicated, it is quite practical to determine the amplitude of the signal level. Make this determination and check it with the transmitter meter reading when the transmitter switch is in the signal position.

The recorder amplifier control and zero adjustment can be used to make the output direct-reading. Demonstrate this by having someone else slowly set the transmitter switch back and forth through its three positions. As he is doing this, first set the recorder zero adjustment so that the pen is on the zero mark when the 0-volt reference signal comes through. Then set the gain adjustment so that the pen is at the full-scale mark when the 10-volt reference signal comes through. Now the signal voltage can be read directly off the graph paper. If the interference level is changed, its effects can be cancelled by readjusting the recorder controls.

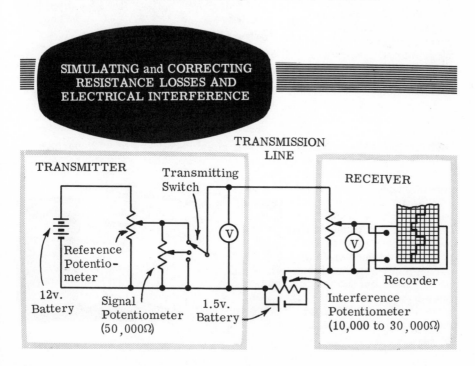

SIMULATING and CORRECTING
RESISTANCE LOSSES AND
ELECTRICAL INTERFERENCE

TRANSMISSION LINE

TRANSMITTER

Transmitting Switch

RECEIVER

Reference Potentiometer

Recorder

12v. Battery

Signal Potentiometer (50,000Ω)

1.5v. Battery

Interference Potentiometer (10,000 to 30,000Ω)

Review of Remote Monitoring

SHORT-RANGE MONITORING - When the distance between a transducer and its indicating meter is short, there is no serious loss in signal ampli-tude or introduction of elec-trical interference in the connecting wires. Calibra-tion of the meter is conse-quently a simple matter.

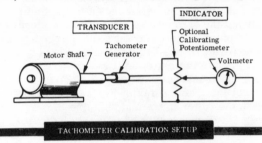

LONG-RANGE MONITORING - Amplification is necessary when the re-sistance of connecting wires results in large losses in signal amplitude. Changes in amplifier gain and electrical interference make it necessary to include with the signal certain refer-ence levels which cannot be misinterpreted. The meas-urable difference between the known reference signal level and the transducer signal level enables accurate measurement of the trans-ducer signal.

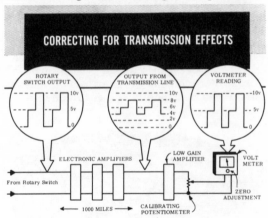

PAPER CHART RECORDERS - Paper chart recorders provide permanent records of equipment performance. Most paper chart recorders contain an electronic amplifier, a recording pen, a pen drive unit, a circular or strip paper chart, and a chart drive unit. Multiple-chan-nel recorders provide the great convenience of com-paring many signals on one paper chart, but the only simplification is the use of a single cabinet and chart drive for many channels.

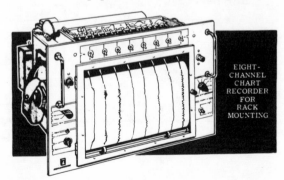

Review of Remote Monitoring (continued)

TRANSMISSION OF MULTIPLE CARRIER SIGNALS - Many different signals can be transmitted over a single pair of wires without intermixing.
This is accomplished by
superimposing those signals
on AC carrier signals of
higher frequency. This technique requires a transmitter,
a receiver and a recorder
channel for each signal.

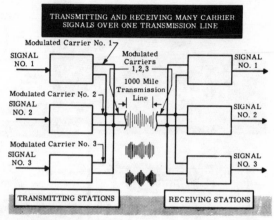

TRANSMITTING MULTIPLE SIGNALS IN SEQUENCE - Only one transmitting, receiving and recording channel can be used if the different signals are transmitted in se-
quence. The individual signals can be identified and
calibrated by separating
them with reference signals.

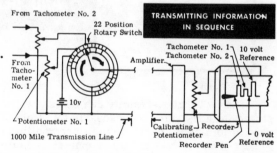

REMOTE CONTROL - Any function that is actuated from a distant location
is said to be under ''remote control.'' You are quite familiar with the concept and details of remote
control. The background
information is included in
this and the previous sections.

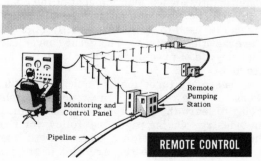

Survey

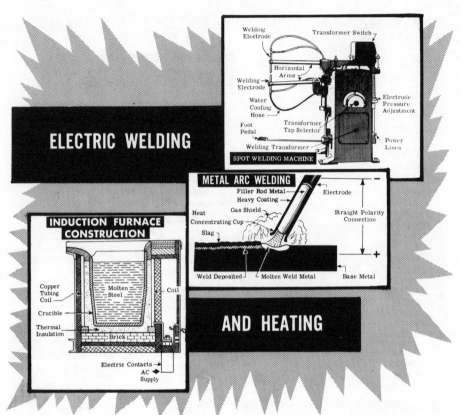

The fact that electricity can be used to heat materials is widely employed in industrial processes. In this field of application, electricity is used to join metal parts, to melt ores so that the metal can be extracted, to heat-treat metals and other materials in order to give them special properties, and to provide a wide variety of other industrial, scientific, chemical and medical uses.

The cost of the electricity required for these purposes is, in general, significantly higher than the cost of the coal, coke, gas, oil or other fuel that could be burned to produce equal amounts of heat. However, electricity can be used to apply heat exactly where it is required and in exactly the quantities desired. The great convenience of electric heating and the high degree of precision with which it can be controlled greatly outweigh its higher cost.

There are three major methods for using electricity to generate heat. These are the resistance, induction and dielectric methods. You are now going to learn the principles of these methods and the ways they are used in industry. On the pages that follow you first will find out how resistance heating is used in welding. Then you will learn how this method and dielectric and induction heating are used in other industrial processes.

Resistance Heating

You learned the fundamentals of electrical resistance heating in Volumes 1 and 2 of BASIC ELECTRICITY. In summary, heat is produced when an electric current flows through a resistor. The number of watts of electric power converted into heat is equal to the voltage across the resistance multiplied by the number of amperes of current through the resistance (E x I = watts). In other terms, the number of watts is equal to the square of the number of amperes through the resistance multiplied by the resistance in ohms (I^2 x R = watts). Variations of this power formula are shown in the diagram.

Wattage can be converted into terms of the heat that is produced. If the number of watts is multiplied by the number of seconds that the current flows through the resistance, the result is the number of watt-seconds. The number of watt-seconds required to raise the temperature of one pound of water by one degree Fahrenheit is equal to 1,055, and this amount of heat is known as the "British Thermal Unit."

VARIATION OF THE POWER FORMULA

$$P = EI$$

SUBSTITUTING (IR) FOR E: $\quad P = (IR)I \text{ or } I \times R \times I$

SINCE I x I IS I^2: $\quad P = I^2 R$

ANOTHER VARIATION

$$P = EI$$

SUBSTITUTING $\frac{E}{R}$ FOR I: $\quad P = E\left(\frac{E}{R}\right) \text{ or } \frac{E \times E}{R}$

SINCE E x E IS E^2: $\quad P = \frac{E^2}{R}$

For quantities of power beyond 1,000 watts the unit used is the kilowatt, while quantities smaller than a watt are expressed in milliwatts.

LARGE AND SMALL UNITS OF POWER

1 kilowatt = 1000 watts
1 kw = 1000 w

1 milliwatt = $\frac{1}{1000}$ watt

1 mw = $\frac{1}{1000}$ w

Resistance Heating (continued)

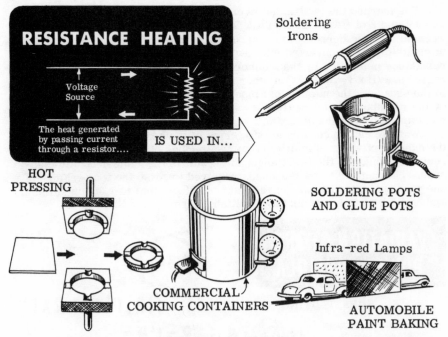

RESISTANCE HEATING

Voltage
Source

The heat generated
by passing current
through a resistor....

IS USED IN...

Soldering
Irons

SOLDERING POTS
AND GLUE POTS

HOT
PRESSING

COMMERCIAL
COOKING CONTAINERS

Infra-red Lamps

AUTOMOBILE
PAINT BAKING

Heating by means of passing electric current through wire of high resistance is commonly used in soldering irons, soldering pots, glue pots,
canning industry cooking containers, commercial baking ovens, industrial
furnaces, printing industry stamping presses, hot pressing of plastics,
and in a wide variety of home appliances. In all of these applications, resistance heating is used because of its great simplicity and convenience
plus the ease and precision of temperature control that it affords.

The resistance wire used for electric heating must have several special properties. First, it must have a high resistance per inch of length,
so that excessive lengths are not required in order to obtain the desired
total resistance. Second, since various heating appliances have widely
different surface areas that must be heated, it is necessary to be able to
control the resistance per inch of wire. This is accomplished by select-
ing material of suitable conductivity and by controlling the area of the wire
cross section in manufacture. Third, the resistance wire must have a
melting temperature much higher than its highest temperature when it is
being used to provide heat.

Fourth, the resistance wire must retain a reasonable degree of flex-
ibility under all heating and cooling conditions; it must not become brittle
so that it breaks under the normal mechanical strains to which it is subjected. Fifth, the wire must not oxidize under normal conditions of use;
that is, its surface must not lose its metal-like nature and crumble away
as do iron, copper, aluminum and others when they are exposed to heat
plus air and moisture.

Resistance Heating (continued)

Resistance wire that is used in industrial applications consists of variations of a few basic alloys and is available in a wide selection of round and rectangular cross-sectional areas. The basic alloys in use are nickel and chromium, nickel and copper, nickel and iron, nickel and silver, and nickel, copper and zinc. Most of these are known in the United States by trade names, such as "Nichrome," "Copel," "Chromel," "Nilvar," "Karma," and their properties are described in the literature of their manufacturers and in texts and handbooks on electrical engineering.

For use in ordinary electric circuits, resistance wire is wound on forms of insulating and temperature resisting material. You learned about such wire-wound resistors in Volume 1 of BASIC ELECTRICITY.

For industrial heating applications, the resistance wire is sometimes wound into the form of heavy-duty wire-wound resistors, as shown in the illustration, and frequently it is wound on special forms to fit inside the walls of a container that is to be used to heat materials.

In such applications, a temperature-sensitive switch is usually used as the basis for turning the electric current on and off, so that the desired temperature can be maintained. If more precise proportional temperature control is desired, resistance thermometers or thermocouples can be used together with electronic amplifiers to form a servo control system. Such a system provides exactly the amount of current that is required to stabilize the temperature at the desired level and to compensate precisely for gradual or rapid temperature changes caused by the removal of heated material or the addition of new unheated material.

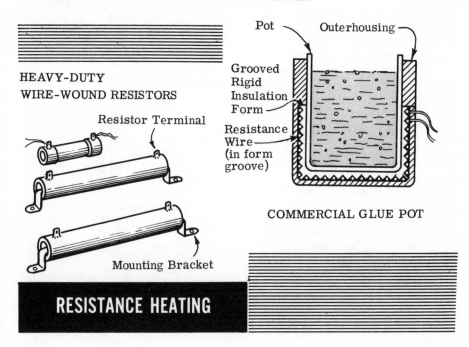

HEAVY-DUTY
WIRE-WOUND RESISTORS

Resistor Terminal

Mounting Bracket

Pot

Outerhousing

Grooved
Rigid
Insulation
Form

Resistance
Wire
(in form
groove)

COMMERCIAL GLUE POT

RESISTANCE HEATING

Electric Welding - Survey

Welding is one of the most important methods in which resistance heating is used to permanently join two pieces of metal. In welding, the part areas to be joined are heated to the plastic or molten state, and the two individual metals fuse with one another to become one.

There are several non-electrical welding methods. In forge welding, the two areas to be joined are heated to the plastic state and mechanically forced to fuse by hammering or by a press. In flame welding, the parts are placed together in the desired position and the contact areas are heated to the melting point by a high-temperature flame. The liquefied metal from the two parts flows together and intermixes to form one piece, with no need for applied pressure. If additional metal is needed to make a stronger joint, it can be added by placing the end of a rod or wire of suitable material in the heated area and allowing the additional metal to flow into the joint. In thermite welding, the areas to be joined are placed in a prepared mold. Superheated steel, made by burning an aluminum and iron oxide powder called "thermite," is poured into the joint region and melts the metal around it. Metal from the two parts fuses with the steel, and a solid joint is formed upon cooling.

There are many methods of electric welding. The major families into which these can be grouped include electric resistance welding, electric arc welding, and atomic hydrogen arc welding. These methods will be described on the pages that follow.

In electric resistance welding, the two pieces of sheet metal or wire, or a combination of these, are placed in contact. Then a high-amperage electric current from a step-down transformer is passed through a small area of the contact region. In that small area, the electrical resistance results in the generation of sufficient heat to fuse the metals together.

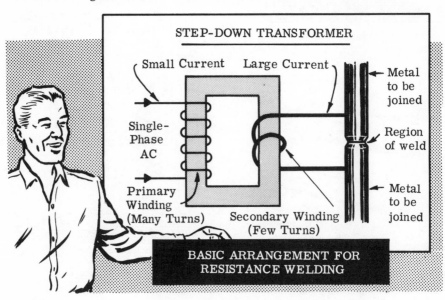

STEP-DOWN TRANSFORMER

Small Current   Large Current

Metal to be joined

Single-Phase AC

Region of weld

Primary Winding (Many Turns)   Secondary Winding (Few Turns)

Metal to be joined

BASIC ARRANGEMENT FOR RESISTANCE WELDING

Electric Resistance Welding

There are a number of methods and machines for making resistance welds, but they all operate according to the same fundamental principle. The basic component of the machine is a large heavy-duty single-phase transformer with a primary winding consisting of thousands of turns of wire and a secondary winding consisting of approximately ten or less turns of large-diameter copper wire or bar. Either 110- or 220-volt 60-cycle alternating current is applied across the primary, and the resulting primary current is generally less than 10 amperes. In the secondary winding, however, the enormous step-down ratio of the transformer generally results in an output of less than one or two volts and a current flow of thousands of amperes. A movable tap on the secondary winding provides the means for adjusting secondary current. In flowing through the resistance of the small area of contact, that large current heats the metal to the plastic stage, and momentary heavy pressure is applied to fuse the two parts together in that region.

Spot welding is generally used for joining pieces of sheet metal. It is also used for attaching many varieties of parts made of thin metal to bases made of heavier metal. In spot welding, the fusion of the two pieces is in a small area, or spot, approximately 1/8 inch in diameter. One or several "spots" are usually sufficient to join small parts, and long rows of spots, generally spaced at 1/2-inch to 2-inch intervals, are used to join large pieces of sheet metal.

The most important features of a simple spot welding machine are shown in the illustration. The heavy-duty transformer is inside the machine housing. The terminals of the secondary winding are connected to the two horizontal arms. Copper welding electrodes with blunted points are mounted in the ends of the arms; in heavy-duty applications the electrodes contain channels through which cooling water is pumped. A foot pedal is provided with mechanisms to bring the electrodes together with considerable pressure and to turn the current on and off as required.

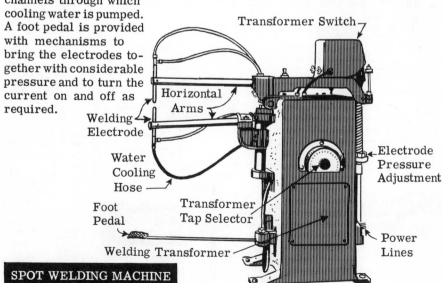

SPOT WELDING MACHINE

Electric Resistance Welding (continued)

The two pieces of metal are positioned as desired between the electrodes of the spot welder. The operator presses the foot pedal down, and the electrodes are pressed against the metal. When moderate electrode pressure is reached, the current is turned on. The small contact area is heated to the plastic stage, and the increasing pressure fuses the two pieces of metal at this spot. As the foot pedal reaches the bottom of its travel, the current is turned off, and the pressure of the electrodes is automatically released. The weld is completed. The electrode-pressure and transformer-switching mechanisms attached to the foot pedal operate so efficiently that a single spot weld requires less than one second. By controlling the pressure of his foot, the operator can time the current flow period to suit the material. This type of weld is satisfactory in most applications. However, because the current is applied long enough to heat the surrounding metal, the hardness and other special qualities of certain metals (stainless steel and aluminum alloys) are impaired.

Shot welding is similar to spot welding, but heat is applied for such a short period that the surrounding metal is not affected. The essential difference is that larger currents are passed through the small joint area for periods ranging from 0.5 to 0.01 second. Because of this short current-application time, switching cannot be operator controlled; high-speed automatic pressure-applying and electronic current-timing devices are required. In automatic shot welding machines with continuous material feed, adjustments can be made to supply a continuous series of precisely timed current pulses that alternate with precisely timed no-current intervals. Such pulses range from 1 to 20 cycles in almost any desired combination, thus providing precision welding control.

Butt welding is a process for making a continuous weld between the edges of two pieces of metal. The pieces can be joined edge to edge, with or without overlap. The electric circuit is the same as that used for spot welding. The two edges to be joined are cut or ground for good contact, and both pieces are clamped to the electrodes and to mechanical jaws which bring them together under pressure.

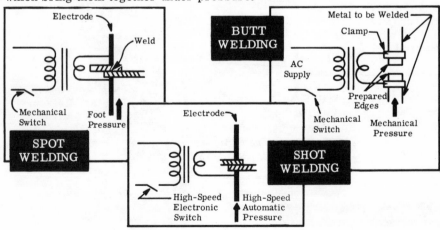

Electric Resistance Welding (continued)

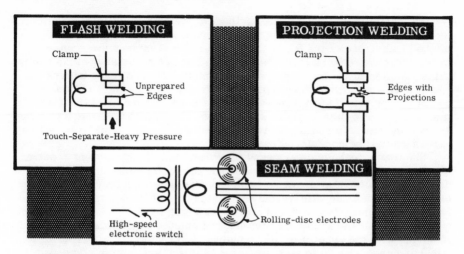

When the two parts are brought together, there is high electrical resistance in the small area where their edges are pressed together. The large flow of current through this line of contact raises the temperature of the metal to the plastic point, and the mechanical pressure completes the joining process. Then the current is turned off, and the mechanical pressure is continued until the line of weld solidifies.

Flash welding also produces a continuous weld between two metal edges. The machine and electrical circuit are essentially the same as for butt welding. In the flash process, the two edges need not be carefully prepared for good contact; they are brought together lightly and then separated slightly, thus creating a continuous electric arc between the edges. The edges are heated to the melting point by the arc and are then brought together under high pressure. The excess molten metal is pressed out, achieving a clean, uniform contact between the edges.

Projection welding combines the techniques of butt or flash welding with those of spot welding. In projection welding, one or both sheet-metal edges have a series of slightly raised high spots pressed into them. The edges are brought together with the projections facing inward. When the projections touch flat metal, all the small contact areas become heated simultaneously, and a series of weld spots are formed.

Seam welding is a shot welding technique that has many of the appearances of butt welding. Seam welding is a process for joining the edges of long sheets of metal. The edges of the sheets are overlapped and passed between two rolling-disc electrodes which are generally from 4 to 12 inches in diameter and which are connected to the secondary winding of a welding transformer. The welding current is turned continuously on and off by the same type of control unit that is used in shot welding. Thus as the overlapped sheet metal edges are fed between the rolling electrodes, a series of shot welds are made. These shot welds are quite close together, usually ranging from 0.25 to 0.05 inch apart, as desired, and form a strong bond between the edges.

Arc Welding

Arc welding is an electrical method for welding metal parts that are too thick for convenient bonding by resistance welding techniques. This method makes use of the 5,000- to 10,000-degree temperatures generated by an electric arc to melt the metal in the contact area between the two parts. Melted metal from the two parts intermixes and fuses without the use of pressure. Additional metal is often added to the melt region to assist fusion and add to the strength of the bond. There are two basic methods of arc welding; one in which direct current flows through the arc and one in which alternating current is used. Each method and its common variations will be considered separately.

Two basic techniques are used to provide the direct current required for arc operation. One method makes use of a direct-current generator driven by a motor that operates from a power line or is driven by a gas-oline or other engine. Heavy-duty insulated copper cables that end in clamp-type holders deliver current to the electrodes. The current output of the generator is regulated to the desired amount by a rheostat connected in series with the generator field winding. Current ranges of from 15 to 1,000 amperes with 10 to 50 volts across the arc are in common use.

The other method for providing direct current to the electrodes is to use a heavy-duty step-down transformer with a rectifier unit connected to the secondary winding. The rectifier changes the alternating-current output of the transformer to direct current. The welding rectifier is a heavy-duty unit, and it operates according to the same principles as the meter rectifier described in BASIC ELECTRICITY, Volume 3. Current flow to the arc can be adjusted as desired by means of taps on the second-ary winding. In alternating-current welding, the equipment is quite similar to that used for direct-current welding. When AC power is available, the most common arrangement is to use a step-down transformer with the electrodes connected to the secondary winding. Under other conditions a gasoline engine or a DC motor can be used to drive an AC generator (alter-nator) which in turn supplies power to the transformer.

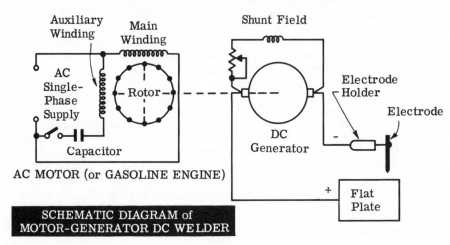

SCHEMATIC DIAGRAM of
MOTOR-GENERATOR DC WELDER

Arc Welding (continued)

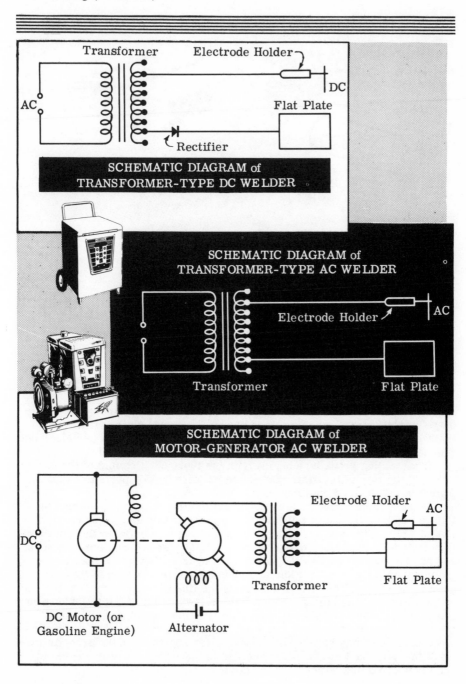

SCHEMATIC DIAGRAM of
TRANSFORMER-TYPE DC WELDER

SCHEMATIC DIAGRAM of
TRANSFORMER-TYPE AC WELDER

SCHEMATIC DIAGRAM of
MOTOR-GENERATOR AC WELDER

Arc Welding (continued)

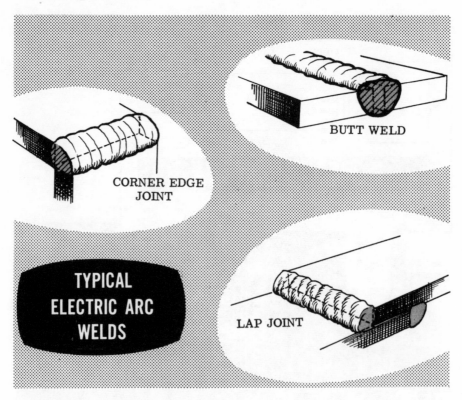

BUTT WELD

CORNER EDGE JOINT

TYPICAL ELECTRIC ARC WELDS

LAP JOINT

In direct-current arc welding, the parts to be joined are connected to one electrode clamp, or are placed upon a flat metal plate that is used instead of the electrode clamp. Thus the work itself acts as one electrode. The second clamp is connected to a carbon or metal electrode.

The welding procedure begins with the thorough cleaning of the contact areas of the two metal parts that are to be joined. The parts are then placed in the desired position.

When a carbon electrode is used, the welding process is started by lightly touching the tip of the carbon rod close to one end of the desired line of weld. This contact starts the flow of current between the work and the electrode. Then the tip of the rod is slightly separated from the work, and an arc extends across the intervening space. Heat from the arc melts the metal in the contact region, and metal from the two pieces flows together and fuses. The operator extends the line of weld by moving the tip of the electrode (and the arc which follows the motion of the tip) along the line of contact between the two parts. If it is desired to add additional metal in order to strengthen the weld, the tip of a "filler" rod made of the same metal may be touched to the molten region near the arc. As the tip of the filler rod melts, sufficient rod is fed into the molten region to add the desired amount of extra metal.

Arc Welding (continued)

Carbon electrodes used for welding are generally 12 inches long and from 1/8 to 1 inch in diameter; the material is usually baked carbon or graphite. Temperatures of from 6,800 to 9,600 degrees are developed in the arc area. Direct-current welding with carbon electrodes is generally used with metals such as copper and its alloys, aluminum and its alloys, monel metal and nickel. This method is also used for joining steel to nickel or monel. (Note: All temperatures herein in Fahrenheit.)

When a carbon electrode is used for welding in the manner described, the work to be joined is connected to the positive side of the current supply, and the carbon rod is connected to the negative current supply terminal. In welding terminology this is known as a "straight polarity" connection. If the leads from the current source are switched, the result is a "reversed polarity" connection.

In the carbon arc methods of welding, the pool of molten metal in the arc region is exposed to the atmosphere. Some types of molten metal, such as aluminum, chemically react with the air, which may diminish the strength of the weld. This undesirable chemical reaction between the molten metal and the air can be prevented by feeding a chemically treated fiber cord into the arc; the gas generated by the burning cord displaces the air and prevents the undesired chemical reaction. This technique is known as "gas shielding."

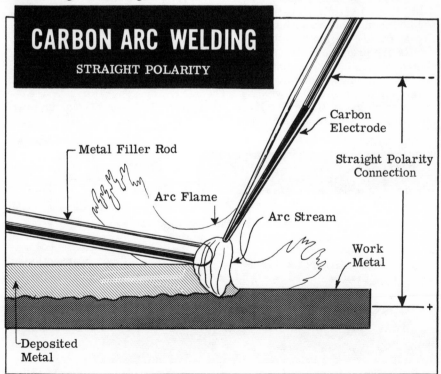

CARBON ARC WELDING
STRAIGHT POLARITY

Carbon Electrode

Straight Polarity Connection

Metal Filler Rod

Arc Flame

Arc Stream

Work Metal

Deposited Metal

Arc Welding (continued)

Metal arc welding is a process similar to carbon arc welding. The major difference is that the arc extends from a filler rod, used as an electrode, to the contact area between the two pieces of metal that are to be joined. During the welding operation, the tip of the filler rod is melted, and tiny droplets of filler metal are carried directly into the melted metal in the joint region. The magnetic field around the arc applies a force which effectively "pinches" off molten droplets of metal from the end of the electrode, and the electric field across the arc pulls the droplets into the region of the weld. The speed with which filler metal is deposited in the weld area is quite rapid, and the work proceeds quickly.

The filler rod electrodes in general use range from 8 to 24 inches in length and from 1/16 to 1/2 inch in diameter. Electrodes made of many different metals are available, so that the filler rod metal can mix easily with the melted metal from the pieces being joined. A variety of coatings are used on electrodes. The coatings consist of mixtures of metal oxides, clay, asbestos, gums, cellulose and other materials. Some of these provide gas shielding, some reduce impurities in the melted metal, others assist the formation of very fine droplets of filler metal, and still others burn away at a slower rate than the filler rod itself and thus form a small cup which concentrates the heat of the arc.

Straight polarity connections are generally used with the electrodes made of bare or thinly coated steel. Reverse polarity is often used when welding metals such as aluminum, monel and nickel.

Metal arc welding can be performed with alternating current, and the details are practically identical to those previously described. Heavily coated electrodes are generally used with this method.

The equipment used to supply the alternating current is quite similar to that for direct-current welding. The AC motor-generator sets are nearly identical to those described previously. The transformer units are also almost identical and no rectifier unit is required.

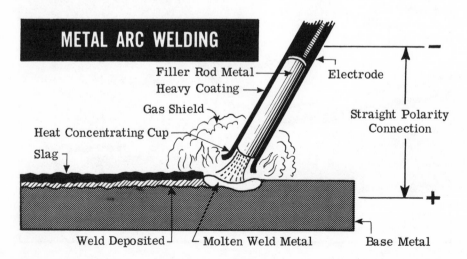

METAL ARC WELDING

Filler Rod Metal
Heavy Coating
Gas Shield
Heat Concentrating Cup
Slag
Electrode
Straight Polarity Connection
Weld Deposited
Molten Weld Metal
Base Metal

Arc Welding (continued)

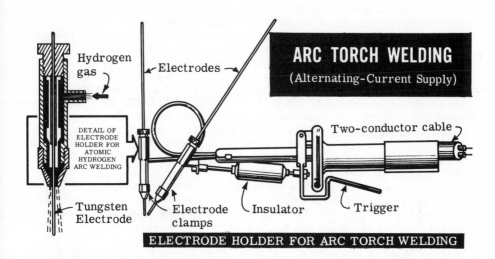

ARC TORCH WELDING
(Alternating-Current Supply)

Hydrogen gas

Electrodes

DETAIL OF ELECTRODE HOLDER FOR ATOMIC HYDROGEN ARC WELDING

Two-conductor cable

Tungsten Electrode

Electrode clamps

Insulator

Trigger

ELECTRODE HOLDER FOR ARC TORCH WELDING

   Carbon arc torch welding is the next method to be considered. In this method, each of the two output cables from an AC current source is connected to a carbon electrode. An insulated handle holds the two carbon rods so that their points are close together. By briefly squeezing the trigger, and hence the clamps that hold the electrodes, the operator brings the electrode points together and then separates them. This starts the flow of current, and an arc develops across the two points. The result is an "arc torch" that the operator can conveniently move along the contact line between the two parts that are being joined. Heat from the arc torch melts metal from both parts, and fusion is completed. Filler metal can be added as required to strengthen the weld. Carbon arc torch welding could be accomplished with a direct-current supply, but the electrodes would be consumed at unequal rates. The use of alternating current equalizes the rate at which the two electrodes are burned away.
   Another welding technique that makes use of an alternating-current arc is known as the "atomic hydrogen process." The method is similar to carbon arc torch welding, except that two tungsten electrodes are used and a stream of hydrogen gas is forced over the electrode tips and into the arc. The metal tubes that carry gas to the electrode holders also serve as current conductors. When hydrogen gas molecules are subjected to the arc, they absorb heat from the arc and break apart to form a gas consisting of hydrogen atoms. After the hydrogen atoms pass through the arc, they strike the joint area and recombine to form hydrogen molecules. The heat that was absorbed from the arc is now released and delivered to the exact region where it is required to produce the weld. As in carbon arc torch welding, filler metal can be added when required. The stream of hydrogen around the weld area prevents air from reaching the molten metal and thus produces gas shielding. Atomic hydrogen welding is used mainly to weld thin sheets of almost any metal.

Resistor and Arc Furnaces

The techniques of resistance and arc heating can be expanded into large-scale heating units, such as industrial furnaces.

In industrial installations, resistor furnaces consist of large chambers of fire brick, heat-resistant tile or other insulating materials. Standard furnace resistors or heavy resistance wire units wound on special forms are mounted on or imbedded in the inner faces of the chamber. Heat from the resistors and from the heated walls is radiated upon the material in the chamber. Furnaces of this type are used for hardening and tempering steel, baking porcelain surfaces onto steel, annealing metals of all types, heat-treating glass, joining parts by brazing, and many variations of these processes. Temperature control of these furnaces is most often achieved by means of a temperature-sensitive switch and sometimes by resistance thermometer or thermocouple control.

The principles of arc heating are also used in furnaces that are used for melting steel and other metals for the production of high quality alloys. Furnaces of this type are made in sizes up to 12 feet in diameter and are used to melt up to 22,000 pounds of metal at one time. The basic construction of such a furnace is shown in the illustration; it consists of a chamber made of heat resistant materials, with either two or three electrodes extending in from the outside.

When single-phase alternating current is used, two electrodes come horizontally through the furnace walls and their tips are close together above the metal to be melted. The circuit and the result are identical to those of the carbon arc torch welding arrangement considered earlier.

When three-phase alternating current is used, three electrodes come down vertically through the furnace roof. A three-phase step-down transformer is used, and each electrode is connected to one phase. The metal in the furnace is "wye" connected to the transformer output. Each electrode thus operates as does an alternating-current metal arc welder; the arc extends between the electrode and the metal being melted.

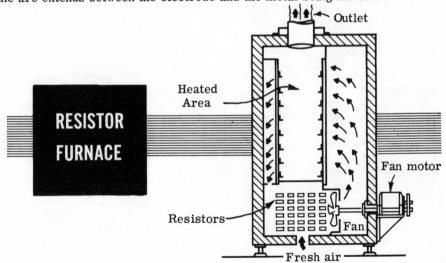

Resistor and Arc Furnaces (continued)

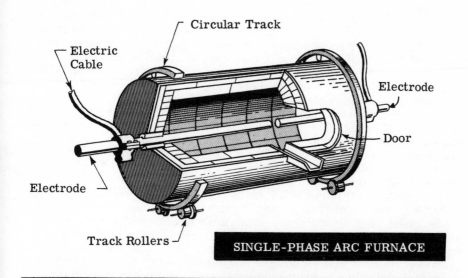

Circular Track

Electric Cable

Electrode

Electrode

Door

Track Rollers

SINGLE-PHASE ARC FURNACE

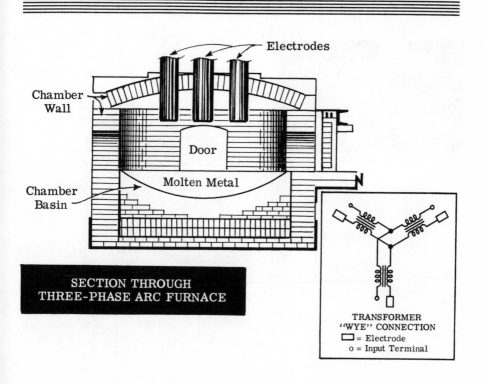

Electrodes

Chamber Wall

Door

Molten Metal

Chamber Basin

**SECTION THROUGH
THREE-PHASE ARC FURNACE**

**TRANSFORMER
"WYE" CONNECTION**
▭ = Electrode
o = Input Terminal

Induction Heating

In your study of electric current generation in BASIC ELECTRICITY, Volumes 1 and 3, you learned that an electric current can be induced in a wire by placing it in an alternating magnetic field. Later you learned that when a mass of metal is placed in an alternating magnetic field, as is the case with choke and transformer cores and DC generators, induced electric "eddy" currents flow through that mass of metal. In chokes, transformers and DC generators, the eddy currents are largely eliminated by using laminated cores - cores made of many thin sheets of metal that are partially or completely electrically insulated from each other.

However, this seeming drawback can be taken advantage of: heat can be generated by purposely inducing large electric eddy currents in a mass of metal. The flow of eddy currents through the resistance of the metal can be made large enough to heat the metal to the melting point. This is the basic principle of induction heating. The outstanding practical example for you to learn about is the induction furnace.

The principle features of a furnace of this type are shown in the illustration. The metal to be melted is placed in a container ("crucible") made of heat resistant material. Many turns of copper tubing are wound around the container walls. Alternating electric current flows through the copper tubing and large eddy currents are induced in the metal in the container. Cooling water is pumped through the tubing to prevent it from being damaged by the resistance heating caused by the electric current flowing through it and by the heat coming through the container walls.

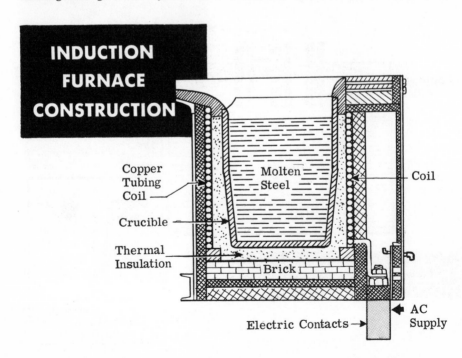

INDUCTION FURNACE CONSTRUCTION

Copper Tubing Coil

Crucible

Thermal Insulation

Molten Steel

Coil

Brick

Electric Contacts

AC Supply

Induction Heating (continued)

The metal capacity of industrial induction furnaces ranges up to 10,000 pounds for steel furnaces and up to 1,500 pounds for other metals. A wide range of frequencies can be used, from as low as 60 cycles per second to as high as 500,000 cycles per second. The selection of the current frequency is in the nature of a compromise. High frequencies provide more heat and hence speed up the melting process. However, it is difficult and expensive to generate large amounts of current at high frequencies. Therefore, the size of the furnace determines the highest frequency that it is economical to generate in the required number of amperes.

There are special advantages to using low-frequency current through the copper coil. Eddy currents tend to flow in circular paths; the paths have very small diameters when induced by high frequencies and much larger diameters when induced by low frequencies. When the eddy currents flow in large-diameter paths, the magnetic fields they generate interact with the magnetic field of the outside copper coil. As is the case in an electric motor, mechanical forces are exerted on the eddy current paths, and strong stirring currents are formed in the molten metal.

Some industrial induction furnaces are provided with both high-frequency and low-frequency alternating current. First, high-frequency current is fed through the induction coil to obtain fast melting. Then low-frequency current is used to stir the melted metal in the container.

It is a difficult problem to generate the high-frequency current required to operate large induction furnaces. The most economical method is by means of alternating-current generators designed to produce those frequencies, but it is not practical to generate frequencies above 9,600 cycles by this method. For the thousands of amperes required by large steel melting furnaces it is impractical to use this method to generate frequencies higher than 960 cycles. For small furnaces used for other metals, the current requirements are lower, and frequencies up to 3,000 cycles are used.

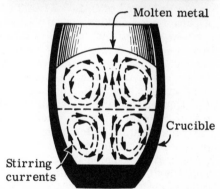

STIRRING EFFECTS
OF EDDY CURRENTS

Molten metal

Crucible

Stirring currents

Smaller induction furnaces are used for heat-treating small metal parts and continuous lengths of rod and tubing. Since small amounts of material are being heated to lower temperatures, the current requirements are much lower. Consequently, frequencies up to 500,000 cycles can be generated by electronic techniques, the current output of which is much too low for large industrial furnace applications.

Dielectric Heating

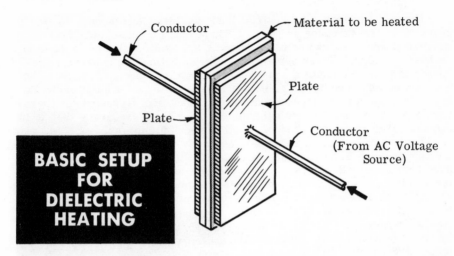

BASIC SETUP
FOR
DIELECTRIC
HEATING

    In Volume 3 of BASIC ELECTRICITY you learned about the principles
of capacitance and the construction of capacitors. The dielectric material
between the capacitor plates is located in an electric field and resists the
flow of current through itself. When an alternating voltage is placed across
the capacitor plates, the electric field continuously and repeatedly changes
its direction. This rapid change in the forces acting on the dielectric material causes heat to be generated in that material.
    This effect can be used to heat-treat materials that would be difficult
to heat by other methods. Such processes include drying and gluing wood,
softening plastics, vulcanizing rubber, drying cellulose products and warm-
ing other materials which are poor heat conductors. A typical application
is the heat-treating of the glue between plywood layers. Since the wood is
a poor heat conductor, heating the glue becomes a problem. Pressing the
wood sandwich between heated plates or rollers is the obvious solution,
but the plates or rollers cannot be heated to a high temperature to speed
up the process, since this would scorch the outer wood. Heating the plates
or rollers to a non-scorching temperature is therefore necessary, but
then the heat takes a long time to penetrate through the wood. Dielectric
heating is a much faster process since the heat is generated within the
entire volume of the wood and glue and does not have to penetrate from
the outside surfaces.
    The heat generated within the material is determined by its dielectric
constant, the voltage, the frequency, the power factor of the material, and
the thickness of the material. In general, for a constant voltage, the heat
developed increases with the frequency of the applied voltage. However,
since the power factor also changes with frequency, different frequencies
produce better results with different materials. The frequencies commonly used in industrial applications range from 1,000,000 to 50,000,000
cycles. Alternating-current generators cannot be used to develop these
frequencies, and electronic techniques are used exclusively.

Experiment - Electric Welding and Heating

PRACTICAL EXPERIENCE
IN WELDING

In this experiment you will learn the basics of welding and arc furnace operation. It is not intended to make you a skilled welder: this requires a specialized training course and extensive practical experience. However, you will be able to see and study the equipment and techniques that are involved. The equipment required is a portable AC welding "outfit," such as those that are available for automobile repairs and home hobby work. Welding outfits of this type generally contain a fan-cooled transformer having a secondary winding with a number of taps, a pair of cables for connecting the transformer secondary to the work, an electrode holder and a ground clamp, assorted welding rods, welding faceplate, welding gloves, and an instruction manual. Available accessories include a carbon arc torch and a spot welding attachment. Equipment such as this, plus a small graphite crucible, will enable you to learn the principles and techniques of electric welding and arc furnace operation.

During all arc welding operations the person performing the welding operation wears a faceplate, gloves and a protective jacket. The faceplate contains a heavily tinted glass window to protect the eyes from the intense ultraviolet and infrared radiation emitted by the arc, and the other protective equipment prevents burns from flying droplets of hot metal. All members of the class should wear protective goggles while observing arc welding and they should stand sufficiently far back to be outside the range of flying metal droplets.

Experiment - Electric Welding and Heating (continued)

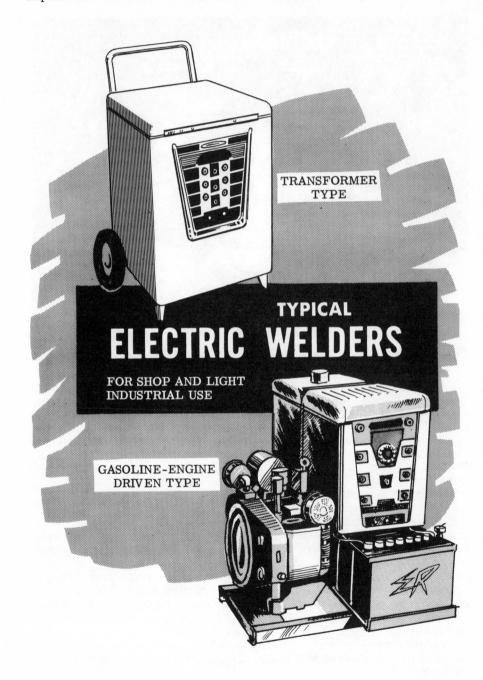

TRANSFORMER TYPE

TYPICAL

ELECTRIC WELDERS

FOR SHOP AND LIGHT INDUSTRIAL USE

GASOLINE-ENGINE DRIVEN TYPE

Experiment - Electric Welding and Heating (continued)

Begin the experiment by reading the equipment instruction manual to familiarize yourself with the particular welder with which you will be working. Since most welding transformers are mounted inside sheet-metal cabinets, you should open the rear panel (or other easily removable sheet-metal housing) so that you can examine the internal construction. Make a sketch of the construction and draw a complete schematic diagram showing all switches, controls and transformer taps. Consult the equipment manual or your instructor for an explanation of any special features that you do not understand.

For the second part of the experiment, arc weld two metal parts together. The basic procedure is described in this section, and detailed instructions concerning the equipment you are using will be found in the welder instruction manual.

The third part of the experiment consists of welding two metal parts together by means of the arc torch. Again, the basic procedure is described earlier in this section, and specific directions for using the equipment can be found in its instruction manual.

The fourth part of the experiment consists of using the accessory spot welder to bond two pieces of sheet metal together. For principles and detailed instructions, refer to this section and to the equipment manual.

As the final part of the experiment, you can use the welding equipment to simulate arc furnace operation. To do this, connect the ground clamp to the extended lip or holding clamp of a small graphite crucible. Place several small pieces of steel scrap in the crucible. Set the transformer to its lowest current rating. Then, using a carbon electrode, draw an arc between the end of the electrode and the top of the metal scrap. If the metal does not melt quickly, increase the transformer current. Once the metal is melted, break the arc and allow the crucible to cool. After cooling is complete, turn the crucible over and a single "button" of steel will fall out. This indicates that the scrap was completely melted and then molded to the shape of the bottom of the crucible.

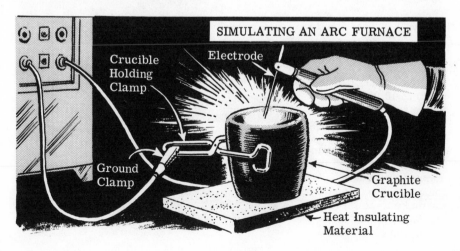

SIMULATING AN ARC FURNACE

Crucible Holding Clamp

Electrode

Ground Clamp

Graphite Crucible

Heat Insulating Material

Review of Electric Welding and Heating

RESISTANCE HEATING - Heat is produced when electric current flows through resistance. The passage of current through resistance wire is used to heat soldering irons, soldering pots, glue pots, cooking containers, ovens, furnaces, hot stamping presses and a variety of other industrial and home appliances.

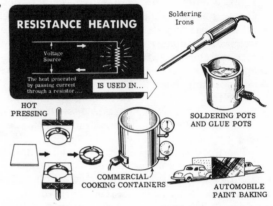

RESISTANCE WELDING - In electric resistance welding, a high-amperage electric current is passed through a small area where two metal parts are in contact and where the resistance generates sufficient heat to fuse the two pieces together. These same principles are utilized in spot, shot, butt, flash, projection and seam welding; the differences involve the techniques for bringing the metal edges together and for applying the current.

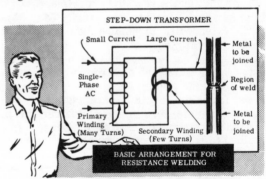

ARC WELDING - When electric current arcs across the space between two electrodes, the temperatures that are generated are in the region of 5,000 to 10,000 degrees. These temperatures are sufficient to melt the metal in the contact area between two parts. Additional metal is often added to aid fusion and add to the strength of the bond. The arc can be drawn between the work and an electrode or between two electrodes.

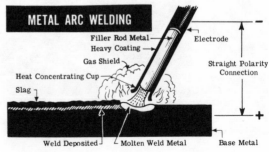

Review of Electric Welding and Heating (continued)

ELECTRIC FURNACES - The techniques of resistance and arc heating can be expanded into large-scale heating units such as industrial furnaces. Resistance furnaces are used for special processes where enormous amounts of heat are not necessary. Arc furnaces are used for melting up to 22,000 pounds of metal at one time.

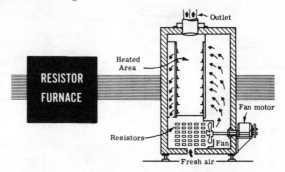

INDUCTION HEATING - An alternating magnetic field induces the flow of electric currents in metal. The heat generated by the resistance of the metal can be made large enough to melt the metal. Induction furnace capacities for steel range up to 10,000 pounds and up to 1,500 pounds for other metals. Frequencies range between 60 and 500,000 cycles per second.

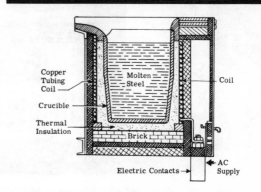

DIELECTRIC HEATING - When an alternating voltage is connected across metal plates with dielectric material between them, the dielectric material is heated. This effect is used to heat-treat materials that are poor heat conductors and are difficult to heat by other methods. Typical applications include bonding plywood layers, vulcanizing rubber, softening plastics and drying cellulose products.

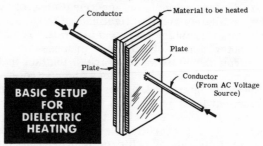

Introduction

AIRCRAFT

PRINTING PRESSES

TRUCKS

MISCELLANEOUS INDUSTRIAL CONTROL SYSTEMS

INDUSTRIAL SAFETY

FIRE FIGHTING

ELEVATORS

Electricity Makes All These Possible

In the foregoing sections you have studied the basic uses of electricity in industry. To round out your knowledge of this field it will be of interest to you to learn about some miscellaneous applications of electricity in industry and in closely related fields. The subjects that will be reviewed here include examples of electrical control systems that are used for industrial safety and fire fighting and those used to operate elevators, printing presses, automobiles and aircraft. You also will be introduced to computer control of industrial processes.

You should be made aware of the fact that nearly all of these subjects involve many different devices and control systems. For those who are especially interested, almost any of these topics is worthy of a descriptive volume at least as large as this. However, to satisfy your immediate interests it will be sufficient to discuss the basic considerations that are involved. Consequently, the pages which follow will serve to introduce you to these related subjects by presenting the outstanding highlights.

Safety Control Systems

Many industrial processes involve equipment setups and operations that are dangerous to men. Many of the dangers are obvious to new-comers but are often ignored by those who are experienced. A visitor to a wood-working plant would tend to remain at a safe distance from the many different saws and other sharp cutting tools that are in operation. He would also stand well back from the grinders, cutters, benders, and hole punches that are used in sheet metal plants. However, the man who has worked with these devices for many years often tends to forget about the dangers involved, and he becomes a potential accident victim.

Some of the dangers that exist in industrial situations are not obvious to newcomers, but are well known to the men who work in the area. Such dangers include walking into areas where men or machines are moving materials, touching hot objects that are apparently cool and smoking in areas where there are explosive or inflammable materials.

Nearly every industrial plant has a continuous safety program for all employees. Such programs include instruction concerning the correct use of equipment, teamwork training in the handling of dangerous materials, and introduction to all of the potentially dangerous conditions and situations in the plant. Such instruction is supplemented by the plentiful use of signs in dangerous areas and on dangerous equipment: "Remove Hands Before Closing Switch," "Wear Safety Glasses," "Hot Metal - Wear Gloves," "Head Clearance 5' 5"," "Hydrogen - No Smoking," "Watch Out For Trucks," "High Voltage - Keep Out," etc.

Continuous and effective training combined with the use of protective clothing, railings, covers, locked doors, and appropriate display of warning signs have done much to reduce industrial accidents to a very low level.

Safety Control Systems (continued)

In some industrial situations the hazard is so great that instruction, protective clothing and warning signs cannot be depended upon to provide long-term safeguards against injury. In such situations, a few basic electrical techniques can be used to force a man to comply with the safety requirements and also train him to automatically follow safe procedures. Most of these electrical techniques require the use of only a few simple switches. These are wired in a manner designed to make operators keep their hands and feet out of the path of cutting devices and follow safe procedures when entering and working in dangerous areas.

One example should be sufficient to show how the use of a few switches can protect an operator's hands and feet during the use of a large cutting machine. The machine is quite simple: Material is placed on a measuring table, and an electrically driven tool automatically cuts its way through the material. The most natural way to use this machine would be for the operator to use his hands to hold the material in the desired position and to press and release a foot switch to start and stop the cutting. Assume, however, that a carelessly placed hand or foot would be in the path of the cutting tool. A safety engineer determines the correct and safe position for the operator's hands and feet, and then he has switches placed in these positions. It is desirable to place each switch on a handle that is used to guide the tool or to guide or clamp the material. However, when a particular hand or foot cannot be made to perform a useful function, it is only necessary to keep it in a safe and comfortable position. All these switches are wired in series with the electric motor or hydraulic valve that drives the cutting tool, or in series with the coil of a relay whose contacts supply power to the driving unit.

Cutting Tool

Material To Be Cut

Safety Switches

USE OF SAFETY SWITCHES

Safety Control Systems (continued)

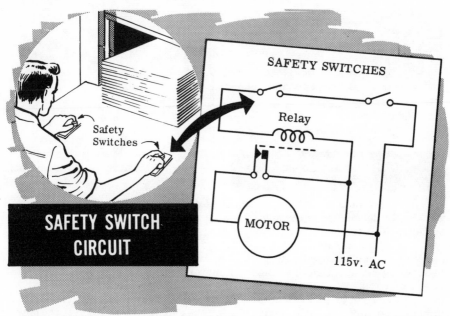

SAFETY SWITCHES

Relay

MOTOR

115v. AC

SAFETY SWITCH
CIRCUIT

Safety
Switches

Now the operator must follow a safe procedure before he can start the machine. First, he must place the material in the required position on the table. Then he must clamp the material in place. Finally, he must place each hand and each foot on the safety switches and then apply pressure to close the contacts. Now the cutting tool begins to operate. While cutting is in progress, the operator may suddenly decide that the material or cutting tool requires adjustment. Without the safety switches he might suddenly reach out to make the adjustment and thereby expose himself to possible injury. However, with the safety switches, the power is turned off the moment the operator moves a hand or a foot from its safe position. If the setup is such that the tool does not come to a rapid stop when the power is cut off, the release of any of the switches can be used to energize a brake or to place a shielding plate in front of the cutting area.

When an operator is properly trained in the use of equipment with such protective switches, he learns to appreciate their purpose and will follow safe procedures when working with equipment that is less elaborately equipped with safety devices. Arrangements of this type should always be planned by safety engineers, and should be designed to provide maximum operator convenience. If the equipment does not place the feet in danger, the feet should not be required to operate safety switches. If only one hand is in danger, only that hand should be required to operate a safety switch. Whenever possible, the endangered hand should be occupied in some useful purpose such as guiding or clamping, and the safety switch should be put on the control that serves that function. Excessive and thoughtless use of safety switches makes operators resentful and encourages them to find ways to neutralize the purpose or functioning of the switch.

Safety Control Systems (continued)

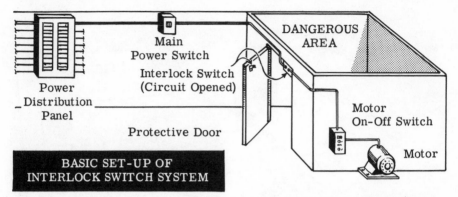

Main
Power Switch

Interlock Switch
(Circuit Opened)

Power
Distribution
Panel

Protective Door

DANGEROUS
AREA

Motor
On-Off Switch

Motor

**BASIC SET-UP OF
INTERLOCK SWITCH SYSTEM**

Another class of safety equipment is concerned with protecting men working in dangerous enclosures. Instruction and warning signs are not sufficient in such situations, and the danger must be eliminated or reduced before a man can enter to perform his work.

For example, suppose there is a breakdown in a chamber containing high voltage connections or some completely mechanical danger, such as rotating gears. To make the repair, it is necessary for a man to open the protective door and extend part or all of his body into the chamber. It might be considered sufficiently safe for the repairman to turn off the power to the equipment before opening the protective door. However, this is not a truly safe procedure. It is possible that a repairman new to the installation might forget to turn off the power. It is also possible that another person might, with completely good intentions, turn on the power while the repairman is in the chamber. The repairman could hang a sign on the power switch to indicate that repairs were in progress, but on occasions signs fall off or are ignored.

There is a completely reliable safeguard known as an "interlock switch." This device is simply a switch built into the protective door on the equipment. When the door is opened, the switch is opened, and power is shut off automatically until the door is closed again. In a properly designed and installed interlock system, no person, regardless of his authority or intentions, can turn on the power as long as the protective door is open. In such a system, a suitable safety procedure is for the repairman to turn off the main power switch and the on-off switch at the equipment and then hang signs indicating that repairs are in progress. Then he opens the protective door, makes the repair, closes the door, turns on the main power switch, uses the equipment switch to check operation, and removes the signs. The reason for turning off both switches, and for hanging the warning signs, is to prevent injury to anyone near the equipment by the sudden application of power when the interlock switch is closed after the repair is made.

There are two basic methods for setting up an interlock system. The first method is to lead the local power line through the interlock switch before it goes through the equipment on-off switch. The interlock switch is closed by the protective door on the equipment.

Safety Control Systems (continued)

When the protective door is opened, the switch contacts open, and all "hot" wires are disconnected from the equipment. One type of interlock switch is similar to a pushbutton switch, and the edge of the closed protective door provides the pressure that keeps the button pressed and the contacts closed. This type of switch may become jammed in the closed position by accumulated grit around the button or by spring corrosion. A safer arrangement is to have an electrical receptacle mounted in the door frame and a matching plug attached to the door. The prongs of the plug are internally wired together, so that the "hot" circuits in the receptacle are closed when the plug is inserted and broken when the plug is removed by the opening of the door.

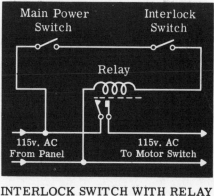

INTERLOCK SWITCH WITH RELAY

The arrangement that has been described is suitable for use with equipment that does not draw large amounts of current from the local power line. If heavy current flow exists, there may be arcing across the interlock switch contacts, and it may also be inconvenient to lead the large-diameter power wires through the doorway. Under these conditions, the interlock switch can be used to open and close the circuit of a relay coil, and the heavy-duty relay contacts can supply power to the equipment. The relay can be placed in the local distribution panel to which the equipment power leads are connected, or it can be mounted in a protective box at the equipment. In either case, it is sometimes convenient to connect the equipment on-off switch in series with the interlock switch. The advantage of this is that a heavy-duty on-off switch is not required and the protective relay can serve a double purpose.

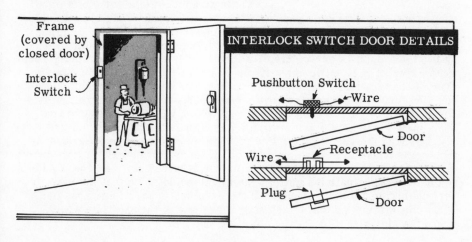

INTERLOCK SWITCH DOOR DETAILS

Fire-Fighting Control Systems

The basic principle of fire fighting is early discovery and immediate application of water or other suitable fire-extinguishing material. A few gallons of extinguishing material applied in the right place immediately after the start of a fire are much more effective than thousands of gallons applied ten minutes later.

During the hours when an industrial plant is in use, it is probable that fire will be quickly detected. Usually, suitable fire extinguishers and hoses located in all parts of the plant can then be used to put out the fire before it can spread. However, industrial plants are not always completely occupied during the day, and they are often almost completely unoccupied at night and on holidays. During such periods, automatic fire-fighting systems are an absolute necessity.

The function of an automatic fire-fighting system is to detect a fire as soon as possible, to apply fire-extinguishing material to the area around the fire, to sound an alarm that can be heard in all parts of the plant, and to send an alarm to the local fire department. Each of these functions is vitally important, and each must be accomplished as rapidly as possible.

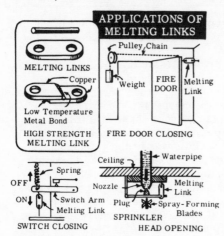

APPLICATIONS OF MELTING LINKS

MELTING LINKS
Copper
Low Temperature Metal Bond
HIGH STRENGTH MELTING LINK

Pulley, Chain
Weight
FIRE DOOR
Melting Link
FIRE DOOR CLOSING

OFF
ON
Spring
Switch Arm
Melting Link
SWITCH CLOSING

Ceiling
Nozzle
Plug
Waterpipe
Melting Link
Spray-Forming Blades
SPRINKLER HEAD OPENING

You can see that the most important part of such a system is a device that will detect fire. One of the oldest means used for this purpose is a metal solder that is easily melted by the heat of a fire. The composition of the solder can be varied so that it will melt at temperatures as low as 155°F. or as high as 375°F. Material of this type can be used to turn on sprinklers, to close fire doors, and to sound alarms. The basic technique is quite simple. The metal can be cast into the form of a small rod or link, or, if greater physical strength is required, it can be used to solder together two pieces of a stronger metal, such as copper or brass. In either case, the bar or link is subjected to a constant mechanical force by means of springs or weights. As long as it is exposed to ordinary room temperatures, it is sufficiently strong to resist the mechanical force. However, if there is a fire near the bar or link, the metal melts and the unresisted force can be used for the desired purpose. The illustration shows how such a link can be used to open a sprinkler valve, to release a fire door, or to close an electric switch which sounds the required alarms.

To avoid the use of power line voltages in electrical fire alarm systems, it is possible to have the various switches connected to a low-voltage circuit that is used to energize the coil of a relay. Then the relay contacts can be used to actuate the alarm system. It would seem that the most direct method would be to connect all the switches in parallel across the relay coil circuit, so that the closing of any one of the switches would sound the alarm.

Fire-Fighting Control Systems (continued)

This arrangement, however, is not completely safe, since damage to any switch or interconnecting wire would result in a failure to sound the alarm. A safer method is to connect all normally closed switches in series with the relay coil. Now the relay coil is always energized, and the energized coil holds the relay contacts open. In this arrangement, damage to any switch or connecting wire will sound the alarm. The cause of the alarm will be investigated immediately and the repair will be made. A false alarm due to mechanical failure is much better than no alarm when there actually is a fire.

In plants which do not have extensive electrical installations, it is sometimes uneconomical to install a large number of electrical fire alarm switches throughout the building. In such cases, the operation of the sprinkler system itself can be used to activate one centrally located alarm switch. A single supply main provides water to branch lines which bring water to sprinklers throughout the building. If a fire develops anywhere in the building, the melting links on one or more sprinklers will start the flow of water through those units. To supply this flow, water must move through the supply main. A flow detector switch, based upon the principles of the flow meters described in Section 6, can be used to activate the electrical fire alarm circuit. In addition, a water motor installed in the main flow path can be used to drive a set of rotating hammers against a bell to sound a local alarm. The water motor is simply a set of blades placed in the flow path and rotated by the movement of the water; it is essentially a blade-type water pump driven in reverse.

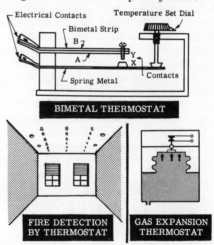

BIMETAL THERMOSTAT

FIRE DETECTION BY THERMOSTAT

GAS EXPANSION THERMOSTAT

Although the melting-link type of fire detector is still in widespread use, it is gradually being replaced by more sensitive types of detector units. One type is the familiar thermostat, which uses a bi-metallic strip to activate the electrical circuit when the temperature exceeds a predetermined level. Another type is based upon the fact that air expands when heated and operates according to the principles of the gas-filled pneumatic switch described in Section 6. In brief, a gas-filled chamber is equipped with a diaphragm or bellows. Heat from the fire expands the gas, moves the diaphragm or bellows, and actuates the switch.

Switching devices such as these operate at predetermined temperatures. The temperature must be set sufficiently high so that the alarm switch is not set off by the high temperatures of summer or industrial processes. The result is that under cooler conditions a fire may have to develop to a dangerous state before the temperature at the detector becomes high enough to actuate the switch.

Fire-Fighting Control Systems (continued)

The gas-expansion type of device can be modified so that it will actuate the switch when there is a rapid rise in temperature near it. Thus the alarm will be turned on at a much lower temperature than the previously described device, and will not be turned on by the high temperatures of summer or hot industrial processes. The device operates as shown in the diagram. It is a conventional gas-type pressure switch equipped with a bellows or diaphragm to actuate the switch mechanism. The major difference is that the chamber contains air, and there is a small hole in the chamber wall. When the temperature in the nearby region rises slowly (due to weather changes, heating system operation, and industrial processes), the air in the chamber expands slowly. Under such conditions, the air in the chamber slowly escapes through the small hole, and the pressure inside is only slightly higher than the atmospheric pressure. However, if the temperature in the nearby region rises rapidly, the expanding air inside the chamber cannot escape rapidly through the small hole. Consequently, the pressure inside rises rapidly and actuates the switch mechanism. A needle valve can be used to replace the small hole in the chamber wall, permitting precise adjustment of the temperature rise which will actuate the switch mechanism.

One major disadvantage of the devices which have been described is that a large number of units are required to monitor a large area. If the sensitive area of each device can be extended, the number of switch units, and the cost of installation, can be reduced significantly. There are several basic methods for accomplishing this.

OTHER FIRE DETECTORS

GAS-EXPANSION DETECTORS SENSITIVE TO TEMPERATURE *Change*

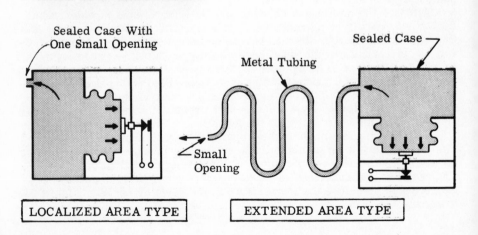

LOCALIZED AREA TYPE   EXTENDED AREA TYPE

Fire-Fighting Control Systems (continued)

The air chamber pressure switch device can be modified to extend the area monitored by each switch. To accomplish this, a long length of metal tubing is connected to the chamber, and the tubing is run back and forth across a large area of ceiling. A fire anywhere below the tubing will cause expansion of the air inside to raise the air pressure in that portion of the tubing, and the pressure rise will be transmitted back to the diaphragm or bellows at the end of the tubing. If the device is to be made sensitive only to rises in temperature, a small hole or needle valve can be installed at the end of the tubing most distant from the switch.

Another method makes use of the low-melting point metal described previously. A wire made of this metal is encased in a thin slotted metal tube that is separated from an outer metal tube by a spiral of insulating material. A long length of this tubing is run back and forth across a large ceiling area. A fire below the tubing will melt the low-melting point wire in the tubing directly above. The melted metal will flow through the slots in the inner metal tube, through the spaces in the insulating spiral, and make contact between the inner and outer metal tubes. This closes the electrical circuit between the two tubes and sounds the alarm.

If it is desirable to have a setup which opens a normally closed circuit, only a slight modification is required. The inner slotted tubing is eliminated, and the two ends of the inner wire are connected to the alarm system to complete the normally closed circuit. If there is a fire below any part of the installed tubing, the inner wire will melt. The melted wire will flow down into the space between the spirals of insulating material, and the insulating material will break the continuous electrical path.

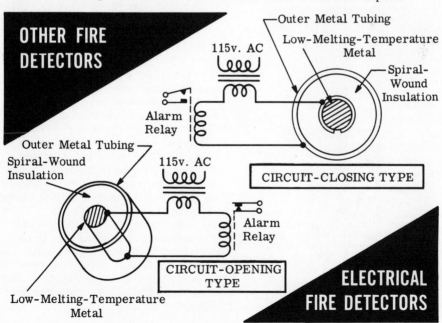

2-103

Elevator Control Systems

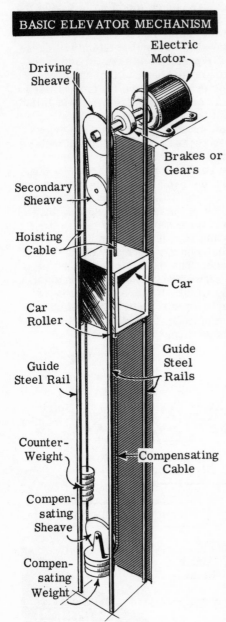

BASIC ELEVATOR MECHANISM

Driving Sheave

Electric Motor

Brakes or Gears

Secondary Sheave

Hoisting Cable

Car

Car Roller

Guide Steel Rails

Guide Steel Rail

Counter-Weight

Compensating Cable

Compensating Sheave

Compensating Weight

You are familiar with elevators (lifts), and you know that they can be raised, lowered and stopped by means of an operator's hand control device or by means of a bank of pushbuttons used either by an operator or by the passengers themselves. Today, elevators are generally installed in all new apartment houses, hotels, department stores, schools and industrial plants. They are used to carry passengers and freight from any floor level of a building to any other floor level, and they are indispensable for efficient use of a building.

Before considering electrical control systems for elevators, it is of interest and importance to review the basic mechanical aspects. An elevator is a chamber or "car" which is raised and lowered by means of cables and pulleys. The car rides up and down in a hollow shaft that is equipped with steel guide rails. Shock-mounted rollers are attached to the car and guide it between the rails. The purpose of the rails is to prevent the car from swaying within the shaft and to provide a surface for emergency brakes on the car to grasp in the event of failure in the normal means of supporting and braking the car.

The diagram shows one widely used arrangement for raising and lowering the car by means of pulleys ("sheaves") and steel cables. This is known as the "traction" system because the driving force of the electric motor is transmitted by the friction between the grooved driving sheave and the hoisting cable. The secondary sheave provides a convenient means for obtaining a double passage of the cable over the driving sheave, thus doubling the friction that is obtained. The basic purpose of the counterweight is to reduce the load that the motor must raise and lower.

Elevator Control Systems (continued)

If the counterweight were made to be exactly equal to the weight of the car and its inside load, the only force required from the motor would be that necessary to overcome the friction of the cables over the sheaves and the friction of the car rollers against the guide rails. However, since the load within the car changes considerably during the course of one trip, it is impractical to continuously adjust the counterweight. Experience has shown that the most advantage can generally be obtained from the counterweight when its weight is equal to that of the car structure plus approximately 40 percent of the normal maximum load. Thus the maximum load on the motor is approximately 60 percent of normal maximum load.

The compensating cable, sheave and weight are the remaining mechanical components to be considered. The purpose of the compensating cable and sheave is to equalize the weight of the cable on both sides of the driving sheave. Since the weight of the cable is significant, particularly in tall buildings, there would be an undesirable shift in the weights on the car side and the counterweight side as the car rides up and down in the shaft. Because of the compensating cable and sheave, there is always an equal amount of cable weight on both sides of the driving sheave. The purpose of the compensating weight is to assure that there is always downward tension on both the car and the counterweight, thus taking up slack in the active cable and preventing "jumping" of the car or the counterweight during normal rapid braking.

In medium- and high-speed elevators the electric motor shaft is connected directly to the driving sheave. Also mounted on the motor shaft is a brake drum equipped with direct- or alternating-current magnetic brakes. Arrangements of this type are used with car speeds ranging from 300 to 1,500 feet per minute.

Low-speed elevators are those which operate with car speeds below 300 feet per minute. In such elevators the motor is generally connected to the driving sheave through a set of gears.

In medium- and high-speed elevators which employ gearless drives, the motor is of the direct-current type with compound field windings or with shunt fields only. Such motors are generally rated in the range between 15 and 200 horsepower and their normal operating speeds range from 50 to 150 revolutions per minute. Direct-current motors are also used in gear-type drive systems, and in these their rating generally falls in the range between 2 and 50 horsepower with operating speeds ranging from 1,300 to 500 revolutions per minute respectively.

Alternating-current motors are also used in elevators systems, but their use is restricted to gear-type systems. Almost all such motors are of the induction type, and the squirrel-cage type is most frequently used. Squirrel-cage motors used in elevator applications are generally of the single-speed type. However, when the car speed is above 100 feet per minute, it is conventional to use two-speed types with two separate stator windings to obtain speed increases of 1 to 2 or 1 to 3. Horsepower ratings are in the same approximate range as those for direct-current motors in gear-type systems; the synchronous speeds of such squirrel-cage motors are generally 600, 900, 1,200, and 1,800 revolutions per minute.

Elevator Control Systems (continued)

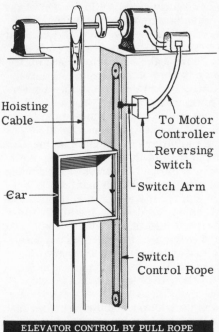

Hoisting Cable

To Motor Controller

Reversing Switch

Switch Arm

Car

Switch Control Rope

ELEVATOR CONTROL BY PULL ROPE

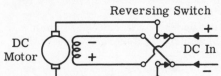

Reversing Switch

DC Motor

DC In

MOTOR REVERSING CIRCUIT

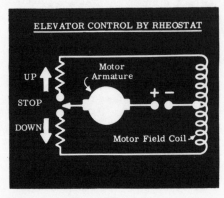

ELEVATOR CONTROL BY RHEOSTAT

UP

STOP

DOWN

Motor Armature

Motor Field Coil

Formerly, elevators operated at very low speeds and were controlled usually by means of a rope running through the entire length of the shaft and through the car itself. One end of the rope was connected to a motor control switch that was operated from within the car by pulling on the rope.

In the simplest control system of this type a three-position switch is connected as shown in the diagram. With the switch in its center position, no voltage is supplied to the motor, and the car remains stationary. A downward tug on the rope passing through the car pulls the switch arm to its upper position and the motor turns in such a direction as to raise the car. To stop the car, a slight upward tug on the rope pulls the switch arm to its center position. This disconnects voltage from the motor, and the friction brake is applied. Since the motor shaft makes a large number of revolutions for a small change in car level, the car stops almost instantly when the rope is pulled. Similarly, to lower the car, the rope is tugged upward, and then, to stop the car, the rope is given a light downward tug.

This control arrangement is still used in freight hoists and in older industrial buildings. However, as the speed of car travel is increased, it becomes more and more difficult to stop the car at the desired level.

Rheostatic control of car motion was the next method that was widely accepted. This method is still used in older and smaller industrial plants, but its use in newer buildings over ten floors high has been almost completely abandoned. The speed control obtained by this method provides a practical means of slowing the car as it approaches the desired floor and for leveling it at that floor.

Elevator Control Systems (continued)

In Volume 5 of BASIC ELECTRICITY you learned the basic methods of using rheostats for controlling the rotation speed of electric motors, and these methods were reviewed in Section 4 of this course. In rheostatic control of direct-current elevator motors, a variable resistor can be connected in series and sometimes also in parallel with the motor armature. Speed control is also obtained by means of rheostats connected to the field windings. In field control arrangements, the motor has compound field windings; both windings are used in starting, and the series field is gradually shorted out as the motor approaches full operating speed. In all of these speed control arrangements it is often more convenient to use a number of fixed resistors connected in series and to successively short out these resistors by means of a selector switch.

Rheostatic control can also be used with the squirrel-cage alternating-current motors that are used in elevator applications. In such a control arrangement a rheostat can be placed in series with the stator winding, although the usual practice is to use several fixed resistors or reactors which are shorted out in sequence by means of a selector switch. When two-speed squirrel-cage motors are used, the use of speed control is generally restricted to the low-speed drive, since this is the speed that is used for leveling the car at the desired floor.

Although the simplest control technique would be to place the rheostat or selector switch in the car itself, this would necessitate running cables or power supply rails with a large current-carrying capacity through the entire length of the elevator shaft. Not only would this be expensive and potentially dangerous to the car occupants, but it would also require a large amount of maintenance to correct the contact arcing conditions that would quickly develop. A more economical and safer method is to equip the car with a selector switch which conducts only enough current to actuate relays located near the motor. These relays can then be used to open, close and reverse the motor connections and to short out the speed control resistors or reactors.

It is necessary to have a trained operator when rheostat control is used. Skill is required to slow the car smoothly and to stop the car so that its floor is level with the building floor. To accomplish this the operator must begin slowing the car well before it approaches the desired floor. In doing this, he is assisted by numbered floor markings in the elevator shaft, and he must judge from the speed of car motion and from the load in the car how much in advance he must begin the slowing sequence. If the car comes to a stop slightly above or below the desired level, an experienced operator need make no more than one or two corrections to achieve a perfect landing. Since control conditions change with the load, with the direction of motion, and with the top speed that is reached in runs between nearby floors, a fairly high degree of operator skill is required.

Elevator Control Systems (continued)

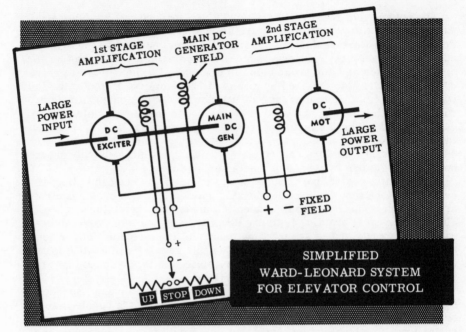

SIMPLIFIED
WARD-LEONARD SYSTEM
FOR ELEVATOR CONTROL

Controlling the voltage delivered to the driving motor provides a more convenient and precise means of elevator control. Another advantage is that it permits the use of alternating current in gearless elevators. The basic technique is to use a high-efficiency alternating-current motor, such as a squirrel-cage motor, to drive a direct-current generator which in turn drives a shunt-wound direct-current elevator driving motor. When direct-current power is available, a compound-wound direct-current motor is used to drive the generator. The entire arrangement is a simplified version of the Ward-Leonard system that was described in Section 5.

In this system, the motor-generator combination runs at constant speed. By adjusting the current through the generator field winding, the voltage delivered to the elevator driving motor can be precisely adjusted. Thus, to start the driving motor, the generator field current is gradually increased, and to stop it, the generator field current is gradually decreased. Because of the magnetic interactions involved, abrupt adjustments of field current result in smooth and gradual variations in the voltage delivered to the driving motor. Thus the driving motor is always under positive and smooth control from zero speed to full speed, and there is little variation of control characteristics with changes of the load in the car.

The direct current required by the generator field can be provided by the generator itself. However, to eliminate the changing operating characteristics of self-excited generators, a separate generator is used to supply the field current. This generator is sometimes driven by the motor generator shaft, and, in large installations, a separate motor-generator unit is used to supply field excitation current.

Elevator Control Systems (continued)

The simplest method of controlling an elevator system of this type is to use the same type of car control system that was described in connection with rheostat control. The major difference is that the car controls now adjust generator field current instead of motor current. Operating characteristics obtained through voltage control techniques are so smooth and uniform that this system is particularly suited to the operation of medium-speed and high-speed elevators. When even more precise speed control and complex automatic pushbutton operating systems are required, it is a simple matter to convert this voltage control system to the Ward-Leonard system that was described in Section 5.

The control systems that are used to operate a completely automatic pushbutton elevator system are so varied and complex that a comprehensive review of the subject could very well require a complete book. Space permits only the outstanding concepts to be mentioned here.

All up-to-date elevators are equipped with interlock systems, such as those previously described, to automatically stop the car from moving if the elevator door or any shaft door is not completely closed and latched. Since car stoppage immediately results in a check of all interlocks, protection is provided against objects or persons falling into the shaft. Passengers or objects within the car are also protected against the various types of injuries that could occur if the car should move with its own door in the opened position.

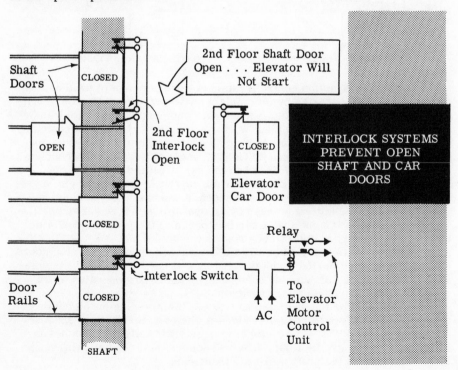

Elevator Control Systems (continued)

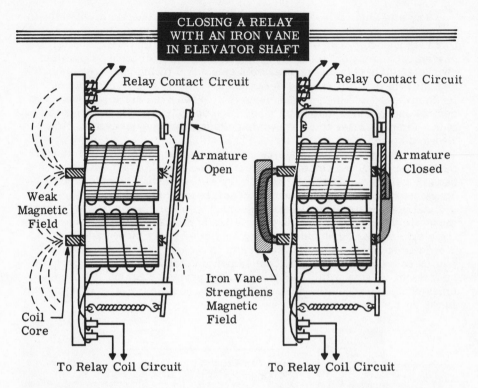

Automatic pushbutton control systems often make use of switches on the car which are operated by mechanical switch-throwing devices mounted in the shaft walls. To avoid mechanical contact, the car switch can be replaced with a relay that is insufficiently energized to close its contacts; when the relay passes an iron strip or an energized coil in the shaft wall, the resulting increase in magnetic field strength closes the relay contacts. In either case, an electrical circuit in the car is closed and a corresponding relay in the motor control circuit is actuated when the car reaches a certain position. Thus the speed of the car is determined by its position in the shaft rather than by an operator's judgement and skill.

For example, assume that a car is stopped at the ground floor of a building. A passenger enters and presses the button marked "12." After a few seconds waiting period to allow other passengers to enter, the doors close. The waiting period is determined by a time-delay relay at the elevator motor-generator, and the shaft and car doors are operated by an electric motor mounted on the car itself.

Besides closing the shaft and car doors, the pressing of the buttons also activates the speed control devices in the elevator shaft. Pressing the button marked "12" in the car energizes shaft coils or solenoids in the vicinity of the twelfth floor. The solenoids extend the actuating iron strips or vanes in the shaft wall near that floor.

Elevator Control Systems (continued)

When the car doors close, the drive motor begins to accelerate the car upward. However, when the car approaches the tenth floor, it passes the first of the activated vanes in the shaft wall. This throws a relay at the motor-generator; the generator exciting current is reduced to one half, and the drive motor begins to slow down. As the car approaches the eleventh floor, it reaches the second activated vane in the shaft wall. This throws a second relay at the motor-generator; the generator exciting current is reduced to one quarter, and the drive motor slows down even more. Depending upon the design of the system, the car may pass one or more additional activated vanes, so that it is traveling at a very low speed as its floor approaches the level of the twelfth floor. When the two floors are exactly level, an additional shaft vane actuates a relay which reduces the generator field current to zero. The drive motor is then stopped, and the brake is applied. If the car overshoots the landing by a slight amount, it passes another vane which actuates relays to reverse the direction of drive motor rotation. The motor now operates at very low speed and lowers the car until the floors are level and the brake is applied.

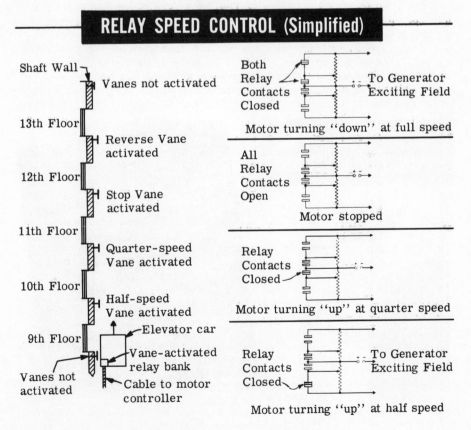

RELAY SPEED CONTROL (Simplified)

Shaft Wall — Vanes not activated

Both Relay Contacts Closed — To Generator Exciting Field

Motor turning "down" at full speed

13th Floor — Reverse Vane activated

All Relay Contacts Open

Motor stopped

12th Floor — Stop Vane activated

11th Floor — Quarter-speed Vane activated

Relay Contacts Closed

Motor turning "up" at quarter speed

10th Floor — Half-speed Vane activated

Elevator car

9th Floor — Vane-activated relay bank

Vanes not activated — Cable to motor controller

Relay Contacts Closed — To Generator Exciting Field

Motor turning "up" at half speed

Elevator Control Systems (continued)

A more highly refined method of leveling can be achieved by means of servo-type control. One technique is for the final stopping device in the shaft to engage the sliding contact of a straight potentiometer unit. Then the Ward-Leonard drive will operate as a servo system which positions the car until the potentiometer sliding arm is at the center of its travel. At this point the car and floor levels will be identical. To obtain this precision type of leveling it is not necessary to use a potentiometer. Physical contact can be avoided by using an iron vane in the shaft wall and a pair of extended coils on the side of the car. The arrangement is essentially that of a differential transformer, and the servo system will move the car until the voltage across the two coils is identical. At this time the car and floor levels will be identical.

Once the car and floor levels match, the doors open, and the passenger leaves. The car remains where it is until a button on another floor is pressed and the shaft control devices at that floor are actuated. When the car doors close, the shaft control devices at the twelfth floor are de-energized. The process is repeated as the car moves towards its next destination.

The car control arrangements which have been mentioned represent only a few of the many possibilities. Systems which employ a number of automatic elevators are often arranged so that the nearest of several selected cars going in the proper direction will stop when an "up" or "down" button is pressed at any floor. Some of these systems are so arranged that maximum service is given to floors where there is a high demand, but there is no stoppage of service to floors where the demand is low. The control arrangements in such systems constitute a major subject in themselves.

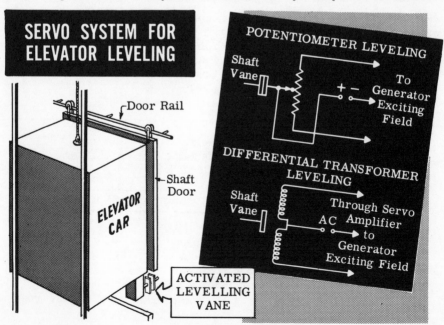

SERVO SYSTEM FOR ELEVATOR LEVELING

Door Rail

Shaft Door

ELEVATOR CAR

ACTIVATED LEVELLING VANE

POTENTIOMETER LEVELING

Shaft Vane

To Generator Exciting Field

DIFFERENTIAL TRANSFORMER LEVELING

Shaft Vane

Through Servo AC Amplifier to Generator Exciting Field

Printing Control Systems

The subject of electrical printing control is mentioned here not because it is unusual or complex, but because printing is a major industry.

The major application of electricity in the printing industry is the use of electric motor drives and their starting and speed controller units. Most small printing presses use single-phase capacitor-start motors or squirrel-cage motors; these are generally operated at constant speed. As the size of the printing press increases, the requirements for electric motor control also increases. The full range of electric motor control arrangements described in Section 4 will be found in large printing presses.

Many printing presses also contain a large variety of supplementary units that are used for cutting, inking, guiding, locking, grasping, aligning, and separating. While older presses employ purely mechanical devices for accomplishing these tasks, the newer presses make use of devices such as solenoids, electromagnetic clutches and small motors to perform the desired operations.

Many small presses print on precut sheets of paper, rather than on a continuous sheet that is unwound from a large roll of paper. When a press prints on individual cut sheets, it is most important to avoid feeding into it two or more sheets that are adhering together. When this happens, only the top sheet is printed; the others remain blank and spoil any document into which they may be bound. To prevent this, modern sheet-fed presses are equipped with a sensitive switch that operates as a thickness gage. Single sheets pass under the switch without closing the contacts, but two or more adhered sheets do close the contacts. This energizes a solenoid, either directly or through a relay, and a reject chute door operates to catch the adhered sheets before they can enter between the printing rollers.

Other applications of electricity in printing include the use of heated presses for embossing and the use of supplementary electric ovens for printing on metal. These processes make use of resistance heating and the temperature control techniques described in Sections 6 and 10.

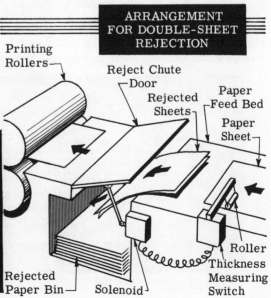

ARRANGEMENT FOR DOUBLE-SHEET REJECTION

Printing Rollers — Reject Chute Door — Rejected Sheets — Paper Feed Bed — Paper Sheet — Roller — Thickness Measuring Switch — Rejected Paper Bin — Solenoid

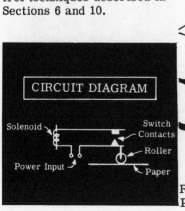

CIRCUIT DIAGRAM

Solenoid — Switch Contacts — Roller — Power Input — Paper

Automotive Control Systems

Passenger automobiles and general purpose trucks have electrical control systems that are quite simple in operating principles. In vehicles of this type electrical power is supplied by a 6-, 12-, or 24-volt storage battery and by a direct-current generator that supplies a voltage equal to that of the battery. The electrical installation consists of three major systems: the lighting and accessory, battery charging, and ignition systems.

Automotive lighting is quite elementary in concept. The driver's area in the vehicle is equipped with a number of switches which connect voltage from the battery-generator system to the desired lamps. By setting the appropriate switches to the on or off position, the driver can control the parking lights, headlights, fog lights, instrument panel lights, turn indicator lights and interior lights as he desires. Other lights are controlled by other mechanisms in the vehicle. For example, the opening of a door releases a normally open and normally compressed pushbutton switch; this closes the switch and connects voltage to the interior lights. Another example is that when the driver steps on the brake pedal, a pressure-sensitive switch is closed, and voltage is supplied to a special filament in each tail lamp. The accessories (radio, defroster fan, air conditioner, etc.) also utilize simple on-off switching circuits.

The battery charging system is somewhat more complex, since it contains an automatic regulator to prevent damage to the battery. The purpose of the battery is to provide electricity to the vehicle when the engine is not running and to drive the direct-current motor used to rotate the drive shaft of the gasoline engine during starting. When the gasoline engine is in operation, its rotating shaft turns the generator and supplies direct current to the electrical system and to the battery.

The illustration shows a typical schematic diagram of a battery charging system. The gasoline engine is started by pressing the starting switch, which energizes the coil of the starting relay. When the relay contacts close, current is supplied to the starting motor, and the gasoline engine begins to operate. Now the gasoline engine turns the generator and current is sent back to the battery through the regulator.

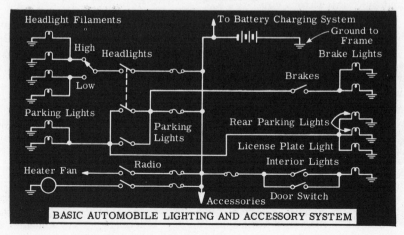

BASIC AUTOMOBILE LIGHTING AND ACCESSORY SYSTEM

Automotive Control Systems (continued)

A major purpose of the regulator is to prevent excessive voltage or current from being applied to the battery. This is accomplished by the overvoltage and overcurrent relays, as shown in the diagram. When the generator is rotated at normal speed, it delivers charging current to the storage battery through the closed contacts of the three relays shown in the diagram. Under these conditions the generator field coil receives its current through the contacts of the voltage and current relays, and therefore is energized by the full voltage output of the generator armature.

If the gasoline engine is operated at high speed, excessive voltage or current, or both, will be applied to the battery. Excessive voltage causes additional current to flow through the coil of the voltage relay, and the related contacts are opened against the force of a spring. Excessive current causes the contacts of the current relay to open. In either case the generator field coil can no longer be energized by the full voltage output of the generator armature. Instead, the field coil receives its energizing voltage from the tap on the voltage divider resistor. This results in lower current through the generator field coil, which in turn lowers the voltage and/or current delivered to the battery to a safe level. During high-speed operation of the engine, the contacts of either or both relays vibrate between their open and closed positions; both high and low pulses of voltage and current are delivered to the battery, but the average is a safe value.

The purpose of the cutout relay can be seen by assuming that the gasoline engine is operating at very low speed or is stopped. In either case, the voltage supplied by the generator is much lower than that of the battery, and the battery would normally discharge itself through the generator. This is prevented by the two coils of the cutout relay. Both coils, operating together, keep the relay contacts closed against the force of a spring as long as normal charging voltage and current are provided by the generator. Any significant lowering of the voltage across the coil to ground or a reversal of the direction of current flow through the other coil allows the spring to open the relay contacts. Now the battery cannot discharge itself through the generator armature or field coil.

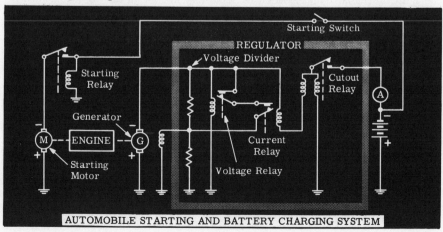

AUTOMOBILE STARTING AND BATTERY CHARGING SYSTEM

Automotive Control Systems (continued)

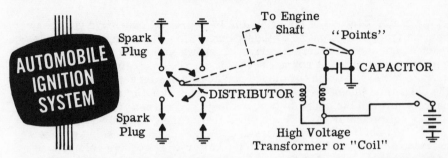

In the operation of a gasoline engine an explosive mixture of gasoline vapor and air is drawn into a cylinder and compressed by a piston. As the mixture reaches the point of maximum compression, it is ignited by an electric spark. The resulting explosion exerts a powerful force on the piston and rotates the engine shaft. The purpose of the ignition system is to provide an electric spark that is sufficiently "hot" to ignite the gasoline-air mixture, and to provide this spark at the proper time. This is accomplished by the circuit shown in the diagram. The arrangement shown is for a four cylinder engine, but the diagram can be extended for use with six or eight cylinders simply by adding additional spark plug symbols.

The ignition "points" and the "distributor" are switches that are mechanically driven by the rotating engine shaft. This mechanical drive closes these switches at the proper time and in the position required to generate the spark in the particular cylinder where the compressed gasoline-air mixture is ready to be ignited. The single pair of ignition points open and close through four complete cycles for each turn of the engine shaft. The rotating switch pole in the distributer makes one complete revolution for each turn of the engine shaft and thus passes by the four switch contacts during that single turn. Note that the switch elements in the distributer come close together but do not make actual contact.

When the ignition points close, current flows through the primary of the ignition transformer, which is popularly known as an "ignition coil." These points remain closed during most of the time that the gasoline-air mixture is being compressed in a particular cylinder. At the exact time that the explosion is to take place, the points open and the distributer pole is almost touching the contact leading to that same cylinder. Now the magnetic field in the primary suddenly collapses, and the magnetic field rapidly cuts across the many turns of the secondary. A surge of several thousand volts is generated across the ends of the secondary winding. This surge jumps across the gap in the distributer and across the gap in the spark plug, and the compressed gasoline-air mixture is exploded.

The purpose of the capacitor is to prevent a spark from forming across the open ignition points and thus burning pits in the polished surfaces of those contacts. A spark would tend to jump across the opening gap between the points, since the collapsing magnetic field of the primary winding induces sufficient voltage across that winding to generate a spark. When the voltage surge begins to rise across the opening points, the capacitor begins to charge and absorbs the voltage rise.

Aircraft Control Systems

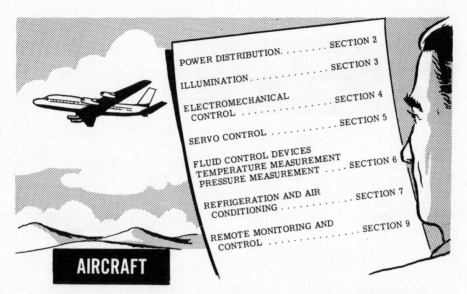

POWER DISTRIBUTION. . . . . . . SECTION 2

ILLUMINATION. . . . . SECTION 3

ELECTROMECHANICAL
CONTROL . . . . SECTION 4

SERVO CONTROL . . . . SECTION 5

FLUID CONTROL DEVICES
TEMPERATURE MEASUREMENT
PRESSURE MEASUREMENT . . . . SECTION 6

REFRIGERATION AND AIR
CONDITIONING . . . . SECTION 7

REMOTE MONITORING AND
CONTROL . . . . SECTION 9

AIRCRAFT

Modern aircraft use many electrical power distribution systems, lighting systems, ignition systems, fluid control arrangements, remote controls and indicators, automatic controls, military armament controls, and communications equipment. Nearly every topic that has been reviewed in these books finds some application in aircraft. Because of the vast scope of this subject only the major highlights can be discussed here.

Temperature measurement is an important factor in aircraft operation. For safe and efficient operation, it is necessary to know the temperature outside and inside the aircraft, as well as that of the lubricating oil and the engines. Depending upon the type of aircraft and the nature of the measurement, the temperature may be measured by means of instruments whose operation is based upon the change of gas pressure with temperature, the expansion and contraction of metals with increase and decrease in temperature, the change of electrical resistance with temperature, or the change of electrical voltage or current with temperature. All of these measuring techniques have been described earlier.

Pressure measurement is also an important factor in aircraft operation. Instruments such as the Bourdon gage, diaphragm gage, and bellows gage and their variations, described in Section 6, are used to measure altitude, lubricating oil pressure, hydraulic brake pressure, hydraulic pressure in fluid-actuated devices, inside air pressure and oxygen supply pressure. Since outside air pressure becomes lower with altitude, a simple pressure gage of the diaphragm or bellows type can be calibrated in terms of aircraft altitude; it is then known as an "altimeter." The flow rate of outside air through a tube can be measured in terms of a pressure difference, as described in Section 6, and this pressure difference can be calibrated in terms of aircraft air speed. A device of this type is known as an "air speed indicator" or a "pitot tube."

Aircraft Control Systems (continued)

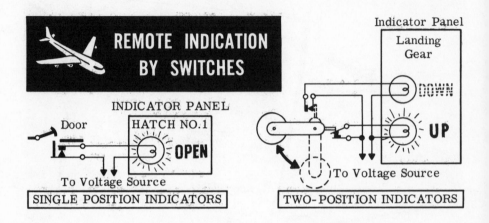

In operating an aircraft it is also important for the pilot and operating crew to have a number of indicators which can be scanned quickly to determine the position of vital flight-control surfaces and important mechanical operating gear. Among the devices whose positions must be known are flaps, cowling, landing gear, interior doors, exterior hatches, bomb bay doors and weapons. The positions of these various devices are simply indicated by having each device close or open an electric switch at each different significant position. Each switch closes or opens a circuit which supplies voltage to a lamp on an indicator panel. Thus, a panel can be equipped with one red lamp under a marking HATCH NO. 1. When the hatch is closed, its pressure opens the switch, and the light is out. In contrast, when the hatch is open, a spring closes the switch contacts, and the red lamp, marked OPEN, lights. When a device, such as the landing gear, has two important positions, a switch is closed when the gear is in each of these positions. Consequently there are two lamps under LANDING GEAR, one marked UP and the other marked DOWN. If either light is on, the position of the landing gear is definitely known; if neither light is on, the situation warrants further investigation.

A related area of aircraft control is the remote positioning of operating gear. Many aircraft components are positioned by hydraulic pressure developed by electromechanical pumps, and others are positioned by means of electromechanical drives. Since most of these devices cannot always be observed directly by the pilot or operating crew, they are usually equipped with limit switches or equivalent hydraulic valves which shut off the drive when the device has reached the desired position.

Certain devices, such as weapons of many types, must be positioned with extreme accuracy throughout a wide range of motion. In such applications, positioning servo systems that employ the various principles described in Section 5 are used.

Aircraft Control Systems (continued)

The automatic pilot is an interesting example of an important aircraft servo system. The purpose of this system is to direct the aircraft along a preselected course and to maintain it in level flight, or at a predetermined climb or descent angle, during the period of its operation. A system of this type relieves the pilot of many hours of tedious and tiring flight control, and he can alter its settings or take over control at will.

Automatic pilot operation is based upon the use of a "gyroscope." This device is a precisely balanced wheel which is kept spinning at high speed by a compressed air drive or an electric motor. The unique characteristic of a gyroscope is that when it is mounted on freely moving pivots, it maintains its position in space regardless of the motion of the aircraft.

The automatic pilot contains two gyroscopes positioned as shown in the illustration. One gyro remains with its axis in a vertical position regardless of the up-down positions of the wings or of the nose and tail. The other gyro remains with its axis in a horizontal position and aligned with any desired compass heading regardless of the direction of the flight.

As the aircraft changes attitude or direction, the rigidly mounted gyro cases change position accordingly, but the gyros within maintain their original position in space. Thus the angular differences between case position and gyro position represent the angular errors in aircraft attitude and direction. These errors can be detected and amplified and used to move the aircraft ailerons for bank control, the elevators for climb and descent control, and the rudder for direction control.

The principles are those of the servo control systems described in Section 5. In older autopilots the changes of case position around the gyro caused changes in air pressure in different parts of the case. These pressure differences were detected by diaphragm gages which controlled valves in hydraulic drive cylinders. The motion of the cylinder pistons was used to drive aircraft control surfaces in such directions as to correct errors in aircraft attitude or direction. In newer autopilots a variety of electrical and electromagnetic techniques are used to detect the position errors of the case around the gyro. Such techniques make use of electrical transducers that convert position differences to changes in electrical signals through variations in resistance, capacitance and magnetic induction. Electromechanical methods, sometimes supplemented by hydraulic drive techniques, are used to drive the aircraft control systems in such directions as to correct the error in flight.

BASIC ELEMENTS OF AUTOPILOT SYSTEM

To Bank-Stabilizing Servo System

To Elevator-Stabilizing Servo System

GYROSCOPE

Use of differential transformers to detect changes in gyroscope case position

Computer Control of Industrial Processes

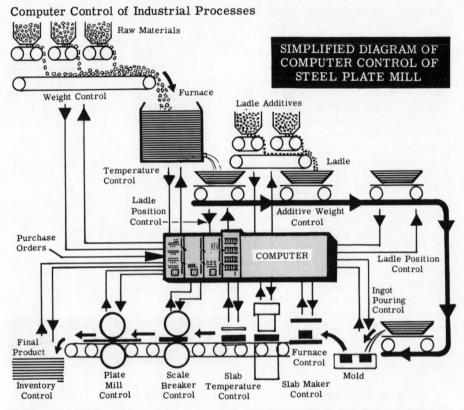

It is probable that in the not-too-distant future many industrial processes will be controlled by computers. Computer control systems are already being used to a limited extent in steel mills, steam generating plants, oil refineries, chemical plants, and in many other heavy industrial processes. As experience is gained with these systems, and as their advantages become more generally known and appreciated, a great expansion can be expected in the field of computer control of industrial processes.

Some of the first questions you might ask about this new field probably would be, What is computer control, How does it accomplish its job, What are its advantages, and How does it affect our future? The paragraphs that follow include some brief answers to these questions.

Computer control can be described on the basis of what you already know about servo systems. By now you are thoroughly familiar with the concept that a servo system compares the output of a process with an input order and adjusts the process to make the output agree with the order. You have also seen how a variety of transducers can be used to check the desired output characteristics, and how the error detectors compare the actual output with the input order to produce the necessary correcting signals. In cases where a number of process characteristics have to be controlled at the same time, you have seen that a separate servo system can be used to control each one.

Computer Control of Industrial Processes (continued)

Many industrial processes, such as the operation of a steel rolling mill, are so complex that a very large number of individual servo systems may be required. Keeping all of these systems in proper adjustment with respect to each other becomes a major program which involves human judgment and the possibility of human error. When the nature of a business requires that the specifications of the final product be changed, additional human judgment is required to make the necessary readjustments to the various servo control systems.

A computer is a machine which can make an enormous number of calculations in a very short time. A computer can be designed so that it will simultaneously receive information from a large number of transducers. The outputs of all these transducers can be compared with input orders that mathematically describe all stages of the desired process; the computer can then issue all the correcting orders that are required by all the servo controllers in the plant.

The advantage of computer control is that all the individual processes in the plant are compared with each other. Therefore, suitable adjustments can be made in all parts of the total process to assure that the final product meets all specifications. Computer control thus minimizes all errors and assures that the product will be produced with maximum efficiency and at the lowest possible cost. Furthermore, the computer can be fed a new set of input orders to produce a product of somewhat different specifications. Then all necessary readjustments are made automatically by the computer.

When a suitable computer is designed, it can be fed all the various purchase orders that the company receives. Then the computer can sort the orders so that they can be produced in the most efficient sequence. Automatic checks are made of available raw materials, and orders are made out for their replenishment. The final result is that the computer takes care of all the details that are required to run the plant.

To keep a computer-controlled plant such as this in proper operation requires very little unskilled labor, but it requires a very large number of electrical, electronic and computer technicians. In fact, one of the major factors preventing the more rapid advancement of computer control is the lack of skilled technicians.

If this field of computer control is of interest to you, your present knowledge and practical experience may be sufficient for you to begin as a trainee electrical technician who will work on the installation, maintenance and repair on the various servo controllers used in such a plant. In the event that your interests extend to wanting to know about and work with the parts of the computer "brain," you should continue in your studies and become proficient in the subjects covered in BASIC ELECTRONICS. If your interests are even greater and you wish to work with the complete brain itself, you should follow your study of BASIC ELECTRONICS with a course in computers.

Experiment - Miscellaneous Industrial Control Systems

In this experiment you will become further acquainted with many of the miscellaneous industrial control systems that have been described in this section. Because of the large variety of equipment and systems that are included in this category, it will be necessary for you to visit several local industrial plants in order to see a reasonable number of these systems in operation. Arrange the visits as before, by making an itemized list of all the systems that are described in this section and sending it to local industrial plants that are likely to have such equipment. Ask them to identify any of these systems that they may have and request permission for your class to observe them in operation.

Before each visit, check over the list of systems that you are going to observe and review their descriptions. Make sketches of the construction and operation and take them with you.

While observing each system in operation, compare your sketch with the particular system that is being demonstrated. Pay attention only to differences that reflect variations in operating principles. Change your sketch to show these differences; or, if they are extensive, make a new drawing to indicate the major construction and operating features of the system. If the new system is too complex to be shown in a detailed drawing, do not hesitate to use highly simplified construction and block diagrams.

When the visit has been completed, your class should discuss and review what has been observed. Make sure to give special consideration to any significant differences between the observed system and the equivalent one described in this section. The advantages of those differences should be reviewed in detail.

Review of Miscellaneous Industrial Control Systems

SAFETY SWITCHES - Industrial accidents are prevented by equipping dangerous machines and areas with safety and interlock switch circuits which turn off electric power when men reach for or enter regions of danger.

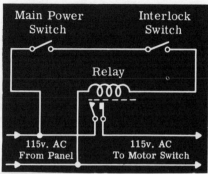

INTERLOCK SWITCH WITH RELAY

TEMPERATURE DETECTORS - Some industrial automatic fire-fighting systems use bi-metal or gas-expansion thermostats to detect dangerously high temperatures and to turn on alarms and water sprays. Gas expansion devices can be made to be actuated by rapid temperature rise, rather than high temperature level.

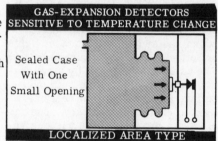

COMPLETELY ELECTRICAL FIRE DETECTORS - Wire made of low-melting-point metal can be used to monitor very large areas for dangerously high temperatures.

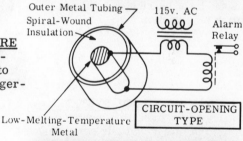

RHEOSTAT ELEVATOR CONTROL - Rheostat control provides the simplest all-electric method for elevator raising, stopping and lowering.

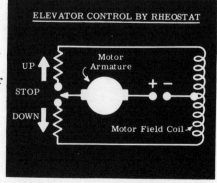

Review of Miscellaneous Industrial Control Systems (continued)

ADVANCED ELEVATOR CONTROL -
The Ward-Leonard drive provides the simplest form of positive and smooth elevator control by an operator. Completely automatic elevator control systems employ automatic door opening and closing devices, car-stopping switch-throwing devices in the elevator shafts, and a wide variety of special devices and systems.

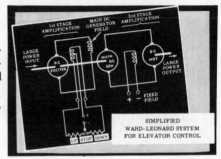

SIMPLIFIED
WARD-LEONARD SYSTEM
FOR ELEVATOR CONTROL

AUTOMOTIVE CONTROL SYSTEMS -
Automotive lighting and accessory systems are simple arrangements which use switches to connect lights and other devices to a storage battery. The battery is charged by a generator driven by the engine, and over-voltage and overcurrent relays are used to protect the battery. The gasoline-air mixture in the various engine cylinders is fired in proper sequence by a distributor, coil and spark plug system.

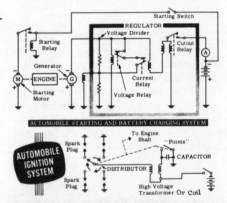

AIRCRAFT CONTROL SYSTEMS -
Nearly every topic that has been reviewed in this book finds some application in aircraft. This includes electrical power distribution systems, lighting systems, servo arrangements, air conditioning, ignition systems, fluid control arrangements, remote controls and indicators and others.

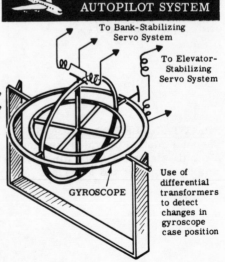

BASIC ELEMENTS OF
AUTOPILOT SYSTEM

To Bank-Stabilizing
Servo System

To Elevator-
Stabilizing
Servo System

Use of
differential
transformers
to detect
changes in
gyroscope
case position

GYROSCOPE

INDEX TO VOLUME 11

(Note: A cumulative index covering both volumes
of this book is included at the end of this index.)

INDEX

CUMULATIVE INDEX

NOTE: The first number of each entry identifies the Volume in which the information is to be found; the second number identifies the page.